STORIES
and
TRUE STORIES

Books by Francis Steegmuller

STORIES AND TRUE STORIES

COCTEAU: A BIOGRAPHY

APOLLINAIRE: POET AMONG THE PAINTERS

LE HIBOU ET LA POUSSIQUETTE

THE CHRISTENING PARTY

THE GRAND MADEMOISELLE

THE TWO LIVES OF JAMES JACKSON JARVES

MAUPASSANT, A LION IN THE PATH

FLAUBERT AND MADAME BOVARY: A DOUBLE PORTRAIT

STATES OF GRACE

FRENCH FOLLIES AND OTHER FOLLIES

THE MUSICALE

THE SELECTED LETTERS OF GUSTAVE FLAUBERT
(translator and editor)

MADAME BOVARY
(translator)

GUSTAVE FLAUBERT: INTIMATE NOTEBOOK 1840–1841
(translator and editor)

PAPILLOT, CLIGNOT ET DODO
(with Norbert Guterman)

SAINTE-BEUVE, SELECTED ESSAYS
(translator and editor, with Norbert Guterman)

Under the name BYRON STEEL

O RARE BEN JONSON

JAVA-JAVA

SIR FRANCIS BACON

Under the name DAVID KEITH

A MATTER OF IODINE

A MATTER OF ACCENT

BLUE HARPSICHORD
(hard cover; later, as a paperback under the name Francis Steegmuller)

STORIES
and
TRUE STORIES

by Francis Steegmuller

AN ATLANTIC MONTHLY PRESS BOOK

Little, Brown and Company — Boston – Toronto

LIBRARY OF CONGRESS CATALOG CARD NO. 73-170167

FIRST EDITION
T 02/72

"James Jackson Jarves" appeared in *The Magazine of Art*, April 1948, copyright by the American Federation of Arts, 41 East 65th Street, New York, NY 10021. Reprinted with their permission.

ATLANTIC-LITTLE, BROWN BOOKS
ARE PUBLISHED BY
LITTLE, BROWN AND COWPANY
IN ASSOCIATION WITH
THE ATLANTIC MONTHLY PRESS

*Published simultaneously in Canada
by Little, Brown & Company (Canada) Limited*

PRINTED IN THE UNITED STATES OF AMERICA

The following pieces appeared originally, some in slightly different form, in *The New Yorker:* "The Credo," "The System," "In the Lobby," "The Doomed Terrapin," "One Round Trip Only," "Ciao Fabrizio," "Bella Napoli," "A Ride with Ralph," "Another Storyteller's Story," "A Letter from Stockholm: The Return of Christina" (under the title "The Return of Christina"), "A Letter from Florence: After the Flood" (under the title "Letter from Florence"), "A Visit to Barbette" (under the title "An Angel, a Flower, a Bird"), "A Burial in Venice."

"Soirée à la Chandelle" first appeared in *Harper's Bazaar;* "Jacques Villon: An Appreciation" as the introduction to the catalogue of an exhibition of Villon's etchings at the Seiferheld Gallery, New York. "Postscript: Marcel Duchamp Fifty Years after the Nude" first appeared in *Show* under the title "Duchamp: Fifty Years Later." "An Approach to James Jackson Jarves" was printed in *The Magazine of Art* under the title "James Jackson Jarves." "Translating *Madame Bovary*" was first printed in *The New York Times Book Review,* as were "A Meeting with Cocteau" (under the title "Apollinaire and Friends") and "In Search of True Cocteau" (under the title "In Search of Cocteau"). "The *Griffe* of the Master" first appeared in *The Atlantic Monthly.*

"The Fair Singer" and "A Real Saint" are previously unpublished.

Contents

STORIES

TRUE STORIES

STORIES

The Credo

Mrs. Henry, who occasionally bought bric-a-brac and other art objects at auction, was always tense while attending a sale — tense when something she wanted was up, with the hope of getting it and of getting a bargain, and tense, in another way, with the sheer necessity of being, at all times, as nearly motionless as possible. The slightest gesture might be pounced on by the auctioneer. "You didn't bid, Madam? But you raised your hand. Oh, you were just arranging your hair? Well, I'll let you off this time, but, *ladies, ladies, please!* Remember — this is an *auction!*" Humorous headshaking by the auctioneer and laughter in the audience, with everyone staring at the blushing blunderer. Mrs. Henry was always tense from fear of getting herself into that fix.

Tonight her tenseness was increased for another reason. She was here for two purposes that were really one — to bid on a picture she loved and to help her friends the Lorings — and for these purposes she was seated badly. Or, rather, the Lorings were seated just where she wished they weren't, directly behind her. Not that they had put themselves there deliberately. They had arrived late, and of the few seats remaining they had taken the first two they saw. It was typical of them to arrive late, even for the auction at which their own collection was to be sold. Mrs. Henry had hoped that they would not come at all, the occasion being inevitably so painful; but she had kept watch for them, even so, and spotted their entrance. She had seen them look around, point to the two empty seats behind her, and hurriedly take them, and instantly she had known that they would cramp her style.

She had turned and greeted them, of course, and, in a private, smiling whisper, wished them good luck; and as they had thanked her rather abstractedly — this *was* an important occasion for them, even if they had arrived late for it — she had impulsively added, "Won't you come to lunch on Sunday? I know this is no time to ask. Don't answer now, but save it for me if you're not taken, and I'll call you in a day or two and check. All right?" It had been between two of the early items; nothing belonging to the Lorings had come up yet. She had been impelled to ask them so abruptly by the desire to ease, through an affirmation of friendship, the strain, the wrench, that this evening undoubtedly was for them. Again they had thanked her. Alston Loring, preoccupied though he was, had stroked his Vandyke beard and assured her, in his courtly, tentative way, "No need to say we'll be *delighted* to, if it's *possible*," and Ella Loring had nodded vaguely. Then Mrs. Henry had turned around again, and the auctioneer had continued to dispose of the unimportant items that at any auction, and particularly at an auction of paintings, are placed first on the list.

Half an hour later, she turned to the Lorings once more, this time beaming brightly, for the first item belonging to them — a very small crayon drawing by Seurat, only a few inches square — had just been knocked down for an excellent price, well over two thousand. "Good!" mouthed Mrs. Henry enthusiastically. But immediately she felt somewhat rebuffed, and uncertain whether she had done the right thing, for the Lorings, who, she saw, were sitting hand in hand, like the perennial Darby and Joan they were, barely responded, barely nodded or even seemed aware of her congratulations. It was apparently going to be even harder to know how to act during this sale, with them sitting so near, than she had thought. Perhaps the emotions involved in selling one's beloved possessions, even if prices were good, were so complex — for the Lorings, at least — that a friend *couldn't* act properly.

The Lorings were touchy and difficult, no question about it. That, in a sense, was why they were here — why their pictures were up for sale. Even their friends and partisans, of whom Mrs. Henry fervently counted herself one, admitted their touchiness, and much more was made of it, or, more specifically, of Alston's touchiness, by other people in modern-art circles in New York, especially those who were on top these days, and who had frozen Alston out, refusing to give him a post in a museum or on an art faculty, despite the fact that he had been — no one ever dreamed of attempting to deny it — one of the first to introduce modern art in New York. People of Mrs. Henry's generation — people, that is, of fifty-five or so — had in their youth first heard of painters like Matisse and Picasso from Alston Loring. In his books, his articles, and his lectures, Alston had stood for, and in those days had practically stood alone for, modern art. Before the Fifty-seventh Street art world of today existed, when there were only one or two galleries that handled modern pictures, he had advised people who were making collections to buy the moderns and had purchased modern paintings for them abroad. He had never taken a commission from either side; sufficient reward, in his mind, was the double satisfaction of helping acquire for his own country some of the beautiful things being created in Europe and of securing patronage for the new artists, many of whom were at that time anything

5

but well off, and with most of whom he had become acquainted during his travels. He made his living, some years quite a good one, by lecturing and writing.

And then — it was scarcely twenty-five years ago — modern art had suddenly caught on in New York; a number of the collections Alston had helped get together were donated by their owners to form public collections, and Alston, whom everyone had expected to be in, was out. In the posts connected with the collections, and writing articles and lecturing as a result of the prestige their posts gave them, was a set of new young men, with diplomas from museum schools — men who were self-assured, full of drive, and very condescending to Alston and his friends, whom they thought a lot of fuddy-duddies. What they usually said about Alston when someone — perhaps a European who had known him earlier — asked why he was on the sidelines was that he was "touchy, prickly, impossible to work with." There was truth in it; Alston had always been something of an autocrat, even among his admirers. But how did the upstarts know this? They had never given him a chance, and his friends considered that such remarks were nothing but attempts to salve the newcomers' consciences.

Thus, Alston had been transformed into a problem, and for years now the Lorings' friends had been ingenious in arranging series of private lectures, private seminars, and study groups to keep them going. The Lorings' pride had not made things easy, nor had their refusal to sell any of the pictures they themselves had acquired during the good years. What would have been more natural than for them to dispose of one of their Guys drawings or their early Corots from time to time? (For despite his fierce partisanship of the modernists, his practically solitary campaign to get New York to know them, Alston had preferred to collect for himself, to the extent that he could, chiefly older masters, most of them French painters of the early and mid-nineteenth century. Indeed, it was his deep love of these earlier masters — his insistence, a thousand times repeated in lectures and articles, that the later, currently more popular men had sprung from them — that had partly earned him the disfavor of the people who were in, and who tended, so Alston thought, to present modern art to the public as a strictly contemporary miracle, a marvel born into the world full-blown, even a kind of up-to-the-minute circus.) But the Lorings had never sold.

Their friends had tried to buy, Mrs. Henry among them. Once, arriving too early, in response to an invitation to tea, at the house in University Place to which the Lorings had lately moved from the studio on Bryant Park they had so long occupied, she had opened the street door, after it had buzzed in answer to her ring, to find herself face to face with Ella Loring, who was just emerging from the basement into the ground-floor hall with a heavy scuttleful of coal. They had made a joke of it, carrying the scuttle together up the four flights to the flat that looked out on Washington Square, Ella saying something about Alston's being a bit weak after a siege of flu and their being, for the moment, without the boy who usually came afternoons to do such chores. But Alston's face and manner when she and Ella finally arrived, puffing, upstairs with the coal had been far from joking; he had been at his prickliest, and the tea had not been a gay one. The old-fashioned, stove-heated flat, charmingly got up though it was, and the absence of the (Mrs. Henry suspected mythical) boy had prompted her to send a delicate note to Ella — a note written and rewritten until she felt it had achieved the right tone — in which she said that Alston, over the years, had so inoculated her with a love of beautiful things that she had to confess to coveting some of the Lorings' own treasures. Would they dream of disposing of just one, almost any one, of the drawings or paintings she had so loved on their walls? If so, she would love to buy, at whatever price they might set. Ella had quickly replied, politely but rather briefly, that Alston would not dream of selling. "His collection is more than his life," she wrote. "It is his credo." Well, to-night the credo, any part of which had been resolutely refused to others who, like Mrs. Henry, had made overtures, was

7

up for sale, in toto, at auction; and since the Lorings had finally come to the decision to sell their treasures, and since they preferred to sell them in this impersonal way, Mrs. Henry was here to buy. And if the little Seurat was any portent — more than two thousand dollars for a few marvelous square inches of paper — the sale of the credo, painful though it might be, was going to take the Lorings out of the problem class.

But how undependable the little Seurat turned out to be as a portent! How misleading! For now the rest of the Lorings' pictures were coming up, interspersed, one at a time or in groups of two or three, among the other items in the sale, and how shocking the prices were! A fine Guys drawing of a courtesan in crinoline — a hundred and fifty dollars! A second, larger and with two figures — a man in a stovepipe hat and his shawled companion — a hundred and seventy-five dollars! The early Corots of Italy, the Barye drawings of animals, and even the Barye bronzes — the very foundation stones of the credo — going for almost nothing! And how pale, or else how very dark, how generally unimpressive they looked up there on the auction stand! Mrs. Henry was astonished to discover how accustomed she, and apparently almost everyone else present, had become, over the years, to the brighter colors and larger surfaces of the later art. Inferior Utrillos, from other collections, an occasional third- or fourth-rate Rouault or Matisse — even Vlamincks and Segonzacs — were delighting the audience with their boldness and their color, and were going for good prices amid noisy bidding. Whereas Alston, who had been almost the first, if not the very first, to bring all that bright newness to New York, was sitting just behind her watching *his* masters go, after a few apathetic bids, for a song. Mrs. Henry sat looking straight ahead, imagining how the Lorings felt, knowing how *she* felt. Clearly, Alston had been too unworldly, too childish in money matters, or else simply too poor to set minimum prices on his pictures, below which, as was common practice, the gallery would bid them in for him, charging him only its commission.

The climax came about halfway through the sale, with the large Géricault painting of a stallion. How often she had admired it on the Lorings' wall, the great white horse rearing, the hostler who was holding its bridle being dragged off his feet by the creature's lunge, the whole thing alive with movement and force and with the swirling, very personal rhythms that, Alston was accustomed to point out in his lectures and to his study groups, recurred, almost curve for curve, in Cézanne bathers and Matisse dancers. Now, behind her, she suddenly heard Ella Loring whisper to her husband, "*Courage, mon ami,*" and very quickly the beautiful Géricault, after a few languid, reluctant bids, was sold to someone for a thousand dollars. A thousand dollars for a fine Géricault! What was the matter with New York? Hearing a sound behind her, Mrs. Henry turned, and saw that the Lorings, their faces expressionless, were getting up and leaving the auction room, apparently unable to bear any more.

It was a heart-twisting sequence of little episodes, that "*Courage, mon ami,*" the rapid sale of the Géricault, and the Lorings' departure — a drama in miniature. The whole affair was so poignant that Mrs. Henry was ashamed to be flooded with relief, along with commiseration. And yet she *was* decidedly relieved not to have Ella and Alston behind her, for in a few moments now the picture she wanted was to come up, and she would have felt most embarrassed in her bidding had they been there overlooking her every movement. The early Winslow Homer portrait! Mrs. Henry had told only the truth in her note to Ella Loring when she said that Alston had inoculated her with the desire to own beautiful things, and this was one beautiful thing that, now that it was available, she intended to own. Painted during Homer's student days, the portrait of a dark-eyed, golden-skinned octoroon from New Orleans (just the glowing head and the shoulders, with a suggestion of lace around them), it foreshadowed — how often Alston had enthusiastically pointed it out! — all the painter's later exoticism, but with a delicacy, an atmosphere, that Homer fairly early lost. "From twenty-five hun-

9

dred to five thousand dollars" had been the gallery's estimate when Mrs. Henry, during the exhibition of the pictures, had asked what the Homer might be expected to bring. She was familiar with the gallery's tendency to overestimate and had come prepared to offer up to three thousand.

Now the picture was being put in place on the easel. It looked flat and dull at such a distance, especially against the garish red velvet curtains, but Mrs. Henry knew how it really looked, how it had always looked when it had hung over the Lorings' mahogany Empire commode, and she hugged herself as she felt herself invaded by the excitement of being about to bid.

"A thousand dollars to begin?" the auctioneer suggested.

There was no response.

"Five hundred, then. Five hundred? Come, come! This glorious example . . ."

"Too early — a student picture," a dealer sitting near Mrs. Henry muttered to his neighbor, and she held herself tighter, gleeful in her knowledge of what the picture's quality was.

"Five hundred!" called the auctioneer triumphantly. "I have a bid of five hundred. Now, who'll bid seven fifty? Seven hundred and fifty. Come, come!"

"Six hundred," Mrs. Henry called in a low voice to the assistant standing in the aisle near her row, and he shouted it to the auctioneer.

"Thank you, Madam. Six hundred, six hundred — who'll make it seven?" Someone immediately did, and then, "Seven hundred. I have seven — who'll make it eight?"

No one answered.

The auctioneer coaxed, repeating, "Seven, seven, seven hundred. Eight hundred, please? Who'll make it eight?"

He and the assistant stared at her, waiting for her to say it, but she, hugging herself even tighter, waited as long as she dared, until it seemed that the picture would have to be knocked down to her rival. It was a device that had brought her luck in the past. And then, at the last moment, she called, addressing the auctioneer directly, in a clear, carrying voice, "Seven hundred and fifty."

The room was silent. The auctioneer put down his hammer and scowled. "On an item of this importance," he announced in the hush, allowing himself the kind of liberty auctioneers do allow themselves, "I hate — I positively *hate* — a fifty-dollar raise." The crowd giggled, and heads were turned in Mrs. Henry's direction. She flushed, kept her eyes on her lap, and waited. And the auctioneer continued, "I hate it, but I'll take it." There were a few more giggles, and that was all. Despite the auctioneer's pleading, Mrs. Henry's rival did not respond; there were no more bids. The auctioneer's hammer thudded, and the next moment Mrs. Henry was signing and returning the buyer's card handed her by the assistant.

She stayed on in the auction room only long enough to allow time for the picture to be sent downstairs to the shipping room and for word of the transaction to be communicated to the office. Then, replying to the assistant's respectful good-night, she made her way out, leaving behind her the sound of lively competition for a dubious bright-red-and-blue Dufy, which, if it was indeed genuine, had obviously not been painted in one of the artist's happier moments.

In the taxi, the picture carefully placed upright on the seat beside her by the gallery's doorman, Mrs. Henry was still tense from the bidding and dazed by the extent of her undreamed-of bargain. But in her apartment those feelings quickly fell away before others. Her elevator man helped her take down a mirror that hung over a chest in her living room, and stand the portrait in its place, only slightly below the level at which it would be hung in the morning, and, sitting before it, she abandoned herself to a collector's honeymoon. The golden creature within the frame introduced no more of an alien presence into the room than the image of Mrs. Henry would have if she had been staring at herself in the mirror whose place the portrait had just taken, and the glints and lights that had been the joy of the mirror were forgotten in the richer and more complicated delights of the portrait — the delights of superlative painting, to which Alston had awakened her, as he had awakened so many others, many years before.

Even at the Lorings', where it had so long been at home, the portrait had never, Mrs. Henry felt, counted for more than it instantly did here, and she smiled as it occurred to her that the position over the chest she had unhesitatingly chosen for it must reflect her desire, hitherto quite unrecognized, to acquire not only the portrait itself but something of the whole interesting *ambiance* of the Lorings — something, perhaps, of Alston's credo.

The Lorings! Gradually, as Mrs. Henry sat savoring her treasure, it began to dawn on her that since they had relieved her by leaving the gallery, she had thought of them only in connection with her particular picture. What about all their other pictures, and what about *them?* "I have faith in the public," she had often heard Alston say. "Eventually, it will recognize a fine thing." What was he thinking now, after his brief, unbearable hour in the auction room? And what would the Lorings do now? How would they manage to exist, with the credo gone and the gallery's check so small? And how — it suddenly struck her, as sharply as a blow in the face — how in the world, if she had found it hard to behave properly with them at the auction, would she behave with them on Sunday when they came to lunch, or if they didn't come Sunday, whenever they did come, as they surely would? She had expected that the sight of the portrait hanging over the chest would give them a certain real pleasure, because its being in her living room meant they would not have lost sight of it forever; and she had imagined, too, that their seeing it there would fill her with warm thoughts of how much her purchase had benefited them as well as herself. But — at seven hundred and fifty dollars!

As her thoughts rapidly revolved, Mrs. Henry solemnly promised herself that she would never forget the thrill of getting her bargain. But what *would* happen? Could she send a check to Ella Loring, doubling the price? Even at that, the portrait would cost her only half what she had been prepared to spend. Was there a chance in the world that the check would be accepted? Wouldn't the sending of it bring results at least as strained and painful as the Lorings' visit promised to be? Or could she go to the gallery people and pay *them* another seven hundred and fifty dollars, or even more? But that wouldn't work, of course: too many people — other friends of the Lorings present at the sale, and even the newspapers — knew the real price, and the Lorings would learn of it. After a few moments, what was, of course, the only, the obligatory, solution presented itself — the solution that was perfect whether it was accepted or declined. Recalling the tense moments of bidding, the exhilaration of winning, Mrs. Henry murmured to herself, *"Damn* the Lorings!" But the Lorings were an old habit, and old habits were — in her case, at least — not easily exorcised. The note would have to be flawless, *flawless,* and since the etiquette books contained no model of a note to accompany a picture acquired at auction and returned to its previous owners as a gift, she would have to struggle with the wording herself.

(1949)

A Real Saint

The events forming the story that I, Edward Arnold, have
to tell will be seen to cover a period of six months. During that
time I was, and had been for several years, a childless widower
in my fifties, and I had not yet met the person who is now my
wife and the mother of my children. From the narrative I have
excluded all passages in my journal that do not focus sharply
on a series of happenings involving me with my father: there
is little reference to the business, social, and private life I was
simultaneously living in New York. I say this at the outset in
order to save the reader's wondering what the narrator was up
to the rest of the time. He was leading, quite simply, a life that
was normal under the circumstances and that was interesting
only to himself and those immediately concerned. Had not my
father and I both been widowers, the events here chronicled
would not have occurred. Furthermore, it was only during this
time that I ever kept a journal.

I apologize for beginning with what used to be called back-stairs stuff, but in Old Norwich, Connecticut, backstairs and frontstairs, in those few houses that have both, are nowadays pretty close together. Highlawn, my stepmother's house, which was old (though, as will be seen, not old enough) and slightly grand, did have two pairs of stairs.

The Will

Old Norwich, Saturday, February 6, 196–. At the motel. 3 P.M. Here for the night.

Counting on Milly's being in bed upstairs and not hearing me, hoping for a glimpse of my father alone, I stopped in at Highlawn — sneaked in, really — on the way to the motel. Dad was out. I think I can reproduce some of Mrs. Rumbold's words. "He cringes to her," she said. "It drives me wild to see a nice man cringin'. And he's the second that's done it. You shoulda seen the first. Your father's a rock, compared with him. *He* made himself a laughin'-stock."

I told Mrs. Rumbold: "My father has never been a laughingstock. For my mother he always did a great deal, a very great deal, especially during her last illness. But there was never anything servile about it."

"Up here he began by wearin' himself out in the garden — under her orders, of course. I never knew firsthand how that was stopped, but I gather the doctor had something to do with it."

"Yes, I can tell you now. I spoke to Dr. Bergin myself, one weekend when I was up a few years ago. I told him my father was always used to working hard, but I thought he was overdoing for a man past eighty. The doctor agreed. As he put it, 'He married her for companionship, but what he got is a full-time job.' He said he'd speak to both of them: my father went to bed for a while, and it was then that they got the gardener."

"My nephew Tom. He's good with flowers. Of course he

can't satisfy her. Who can? Thank the Lord you stepped in. Otherwise she'd a killed your father."

"And now I'm afraid it's she who's on the way out."

"Oh, she's failin'. I think maybe her mind's failin' even faster'n the rest of her, she's so *infernally* nasty. Of course she was always so nasty anyway it's hard to tell. Mrs. Hanes tell you about the fracas over the Jell-O salad yesterday?"

"I just arrived from New York. I haven't seen Mrs. Hanes."

"She said she was going to phone you in the city. I didn't suppose she would, once she cooled down. But she was capable of it. You won't see her around here no more, unless he persuades her to come back. That's where he is now, down at her house eatin' humble pie, as he oughta. Been gone since just after lunch, must be having quite a powwow. He didn't stick up for either of us when Her Majesty threw the lime Jell-O salad on the floor. He didn't tell her it was him had ordered it specially because he thought it would please her. He let us take the blame. We were both down on him yesterday. Maybe Mrs. Hanes will come back, out of regard for him. We both think a lot of him. It's more sad than anything else, seeing a man's self-respect bein' whittled away."

At that point there was a tapping on the ceiling. "I'll run up and see what she wants," said Mrs. Rumbold. "Should I tell her you're here?"

"Better not. You know what it does to her to think I've been having a word alone with any of you. I'll drop in for cocktails later, as usual, as though I'd just that moment arrived."

I let myself out quietly and drove down the road to the motel. On the way I saw my father's Buick approaching, and honked, but he and Mrs. Hanes, together in the front seat, were too absorbed in conversation to notice. Seeing them driving and talking together like that, anyone might have supposed them man and wife. I wonder: would Dad have been happier with some nice houseworker like Mrs. Rumbold or a practical nurse like Mrs. Hanes than married into Old Norwich's "aristocracy," as he calls Milly and her circle? Easy to picture my mother the pretty young schoolteacher she was when my father married her. Impossible to picture poor Milly the debutante *she* was, years ago.

Same day. 10 P.M. At Highlawn. Not spending the night at the motel, after all. Quite a development. Arrived here at Highlawn about five, expecting the usual whiskey sours beside the fire. Found Mrs. Rumbold and Mrs. Hanes waiting for me in the front hall. Sudden death! The tapping on the ceiling was taps. "By the time I got there she was gone," said Mrs. Rumbold. And by now Milly was *totally* gone — out of the house. Mr. Riley, the undertaker, had come in after Dr. Bergin had left, and removed her. "Never saw so much happen so fast in my life," said Mrs. Rumbold. "You know she's to be buried in New Jersey, next to her first," Mrs. Hanes said. "It seemed queer not telephoning you, but your dad said absolutely not." The women became antiphonal. "He said you'd be coming anyway, so what was the use." "She was seventy-seven. The doctor knew — nobody else did." "She never appreciated how good she had it these last years, with your dad." "I guess her bark was worse than her bite, poor thing." "But boy, was she ever a barker, no use pretendin'."

I saw my father coming down the stairs.

"Dad, what can I say?"

"May she rest in peace."

"May she rest in peace."

The two women echoed: "May she rest in peace."

The old man looked frail, but handsome as ever, tall and erect at eighty-eight, his hair very white. "Suppose you make the cocktails today, Ed." And beside the fire, with the usual little table drawn up, with the usual dishes of olives and nuts, with two chairs instead of three, he raised his first whiskey sour in his knotty hand: "To her immortal soul."

"Amen."

It reminded me of priests I used to see at the New York Athletic Club, crossing themselves before a meal — i.e., over their martinis.

I asked him: "Shall I bring my things from the motel and sleep here?"

The pause before his answer made me wonder: was my offer unseemly, a too-quick flouting of the deceased? (I must remind myself, lest I forget, how strictly, exclusively Saturday-cocktail the Highlawn hospitality has always been, in the infrequent ritual of my visits. Dinner or the night was unthinkable. The only occasional dividend, a brief, near-furtive Sunday-morning dropping-in by the old man to see me at the motel after Mass, scarcely frequent enough to be worth my sleeping-over for. Even with those bare bones of maintained relations, my coming always brought the danger of Milly-tantrums.)

"I don't think anybody would mind," my father said.

Mrs. Rumbold's face, when she was asked to make up a bed in a guest room, registered the full import of the request — of the change. "You'll have supper here?" she asked. "There's an extra chop." "All this and her lamb chop too," she seemed to be thinking — not without approval, perhaps.

The old man was tired, and we didn't say much. He had telephoned the cousins in New Jersey. They, their pastor (Congregational), and Riley the undertaker would arrange things among them, and then the widower would drive himself down to attend the laying-to-rest of his second wife beside her first husband. "A good arrangement," Dad called it. It took me a little time to realize that he was referring to eternity, where the two couples could thus meet without embarrassment. After supper he opened his *Catholic Transcript*, and when I came back from checking out of the motel Mrs. Rumbold and Mrs. Hanes bade us good-night and drove away together.

"Just when I persuaded Mrs. Hanes to stay. Now I'll have to tell her she's no longer needed."

"I'm sure she knows that already. But why not keep her on a few days, to help sort things out and so on, if she's willing?" (I was really thinking that he might need a little attention himself.) "The clothes . . ."

"If she and Mrs. Rumbold worked fast I could take the clothes with me — to New Jersey. That's where they're to go, apparently."

"They've already been mentioned? On the telephone?"

"I mentioned them. Without thinking, I said I supposed I'd be taking the clothes to St. Clare's Shelter. There was an immediate request — sounded more like an order — that I do no such thing. I didn't point out that for years even the Protestant churches around here have let me cart their left-over clothes from rummage sales to St. Clare's, Catholic though it is. I just said OK, it would be as they wished."

We said good-night at the top of the stairs. Just now as I crossed the hall from the bath, Dad's door was open and he was on his knees beside his bed — a sight I hadn't seen for years. Disquieting, just as it always used to be. Why?

This guest room has the unmistakable air of long time no guests.

East 61st Street, Sunday evening, February 7. Made break-fast at Highlawn, drove Dad to Mass, read the *New York Times* in the car outside the church, took him for a drive along the frozen river and to a log-cabin restaurant for spaghetti and meatballs. It was crowded with beer-drinking ice-hole fishermen in lumberjack shirts. "Lord," Dad said, "did Milly hate surroundings like these. She'd say it was 'trashy' here, God rest her soul."

"Amen. When did you go fishing last?"

"Not since you gave me my permanent license."

That was his eighty-fifth birthday present from me, given the same weekend I spoke to Dr. Bergin. A tantrum-pro-voking combination, I fear; probably something like "Too frail to garden, but quite able to fish!" was spat out at him.

He refused to ask anybody to spend the night, and as

twilight fell even threw out hints of being impatient to be left alone. "I thought you hated night driving. Getting pretty dark for the road," etc. We said good-bye at the front door. Walking toward my car I saw that another car had entered the drive; its lights had apparently just been extinguished, and its occupant was emerging. I knew him by sight. "Oh, Father Healy, good evening."

"Hello." There was no cordiality: of course he knew from my father what a renegade I was.

"Let me switch on my lights, Father; they'll brighten the path to the front door."

"Don't bother. I know my way."

I did switch on my lights, and they did cast a beam toward the front of the house. But at the same moment the back-porch light went on, and I saw Dad standing in the open back door. The priest made his way in that direction as I drove off. Hadn't Dad's silence about Father Healy's obviously expected visit been rather an exaggeration? Of course my alienation from the Church has always pained him, but he's never before behaved so oddly in connection with it.

Driving down the parkway I thought that Dad could probably do with a change, and wondered where we might go. A change — not a rest. I'm sure that frailty hasn't altered the old man's scorn for the concept of rest as a commodity to be paid for. When I think of my taking him to Barbados after Mother's death a dozen years ago! I assumed the trip would be accepted as a bit of rest and change. Never will I forget, after breakfast the first morning, his staring at the hotel guests stretched out in rows of deck chairs. "What are they all doing?" "Nothing. Sunbathing. Resting." *"Resting? Oh."* The pall that accumulated during the following days, despite all the swimming, sailing, drives to cliffs, to plantation houses and "quaint parish churches"! His limit of endurance was reached one afternoon when we were (as usual) passing a sugarcane field. Dad asked the driver to stop. He got out without a word to me and walked over to the foreman of the line of sweating black cutters. "Mind if I try out one of the knives?" "Not at all, sir. Ralph!" In the line, in sullen Ralph's place and with Ralph's machete, he watched for a moment, slashed experimentally, then steadily, on and on, until the women in the hitherto stony-faced gang began a giggling that swelled into a *tutti* of whoops and cheers. He returned to the car dripping, to a chorus of "Good mahn!" Thereafter he referred to the dollar he slipped the grinning foreman as "the one worthwhile expenditure of the trip." The concept of expensive rest, so utterly inane, seemed to endow the Barbados fortnight with a kind of anonymity in his mind: on arrival at the airport in New York, when the Immigration Officer put the usual question, "Where have you been?" he turned to me and asked, "Where were we, anyway?" He's less physically restless now, but there's no question of trying another reposeful isle.

Highlawn, Saturday, February 13. The lawyer's office is in one of Old Norwich's trim little 1810 pediment-fronts, its white clapboards and green shutters glistening, the ground floor curetted and fitted with partitions, filing cabinets, and electric typewriters. Upstairs, cretonne curtains and maple in the private offices and conference rooms. "Glad you're here," young Amesbury murmured privately to me. "When your dad said you'd be coming up this weekend I took the liberty of suggesting that he bring you. I know he's a sturdy character, but today he may be glad of a little support. By God I pled with that woman about her will but she was like a stone wall."

"It's unusual, though not unheard-of, for one spouse to keep his or her testamentary intentions unknown to the other," Amesbury began when the three of us were seated. "I know that you, sir, made Mrs. Arnold familiar with your will, but for reasons best known to herself she preferred to play her hand differently. When I read her will now it will, I think, be the first time you hear its contents?"

"Except that she discussed a few details with me. I always told her that her will was strictly her business, and to disregard me completely if she wished."

"She couldn't do quite that, even if she had so wished. Spouses have rights, in this state at least. There is another unusual feature of the present case. Mrs. Arnold's cousins, the Misses Kirkup of New Jersey, are beneficiaries under this will, and as such I of course invited them here today to be present at the reading. They declined to come. They told me there was no need for them to make the trip, as they were quite familiar with the terms, having been sent a copy of the will by Mrs. Arnold herself shortly after it was made. I checked with them over the telephone, and there's no doubt that what they have is an accurate copy of this document. Did you know that Mrs. Arnold had had a copy made and sent to them, Mr. Arnold?"

"No."

"Nor did I, or anyone in this office."

"But, once again, I always told her everything concerning her will was strictly her business."

"But, once again, sir, that is not strictly true. You as a spouse have rights, which as you will see have been protected. Well, shall I read?"

Amesbury read.

When he finished, there was a silence, then Amesbury said, "What would have been more normal, in my opinion, since you have reached what must be called an advanced age, and what I suggested very strongly to Mrs. Arnold, was that everything be left to you in trust for the remainder of your life, then go to the Misses Kirkup in toto. More peaceful for you. And eventually to their advantage as well. But she preferred the present formula. This was a new, changed will. I believe the earlier ones were made in New Jersey."

My father turned to me: "Now I remember how they phrased it over the telephone — 'Everything is to come to us.' I took it to be an expression of preference, a surprisingly arrogant expression, I thought it, about the clothes — that they go not to St. Clare's but to some charity of their own. Little did I realize that they were merely claiming for themselves what was theirs, since to them go the entire contents of Highlawn 'at everyone's earliest convenience.' Wasn't that the phrase?" he asked Amesbury.

"Correct."

It was unmistakable that my father was criticizing no one, not even the testatrix, but rather apologizing to the other legatees for having mistakenly accused them, to me, of an offense to St. Clare's Shelter, the women's part of a Franciscan home for the homeless on the Hudson that he had long been indefatigable in providing with clothes. "You know I saw the Miss Kirkups at the funeral, just three days ago," he said to Amesbury. "I spent several harmonious hours with them, as I hope to again. Nothing was said about their knowledge of the will. Let me be sure I have one or two things straight. The entire portfolio of securities, and all bank accounts, to the Miss Kirkups?"

"Correct."

"The entire contents of Highlawn to them?"

"Correct. 'At everyone's earliest convenience,' as you correctly quoted."

"Highlawn itself to me."

"Correct."

Dad seemed puzzled. "Those provisions include just the details Mrs. Arnold discussed with me. I don't know whether you know that I brought a small principal with me when we married, after my retirement from business — the sale price of the house owned by my first wife and myself. I drew on that principal to pay my share of running Highlawn and for general expenses. Just at the time this will was made my money was about exhausted. In discussing this will she was about to make, Mrs. Arnold mentioned that if she were to leave me Highlawn and no income I'd have to sell or rent the house immediately and move out, and she pointed out particularly that such testamentary provision would make it impossible for me to bring my sister to live here with me. You know I have an unmarried sister, the only one left of the ten of us boys and girls. Mrs. Arnold mentioned those details in a thoughtful way, I remember; it seemed to me she was running over things that she must *not* do, feeling her way toward just the kind of will she wanted. It puzzles me that . . . It's true she never cared particularly for my sister, but still . . . I hope you don't think I'm complaining. It's a big thing for her to have left me the house. She didn't have to. I always told her . . ."

It seemed to me that only I, with my long memories of my mother's headshakings about my father's deep-grained innocence that had always been so disastrous in business, and his incorrigible turning of the other cheek to all and sundry, could credit the sincerity of his not "complaining" about a will that coupled what amounted to lifelong provision with disruption and insult. God knows that Aunt Anna, now a lay boarder in a Hartford convent after years as a priest's housekeeper, was never a very bright light. (When she kissed me at my mother's funeral she lamented: "And just when your father had the whole house repapered!") But only by a very strange mind indeed could her person be thought of as threatening pollution to Highlawn. However, like Dr. Bergin and his "He married her for companionship, but what he got is a full-time job," and like Mrs. Rumbold and Mrs. Hanes, young Amesbury now displayed his share of the general esteem that Dad has obviously inspired during his years in Old Norwich.

"I take it, sir, that you have no intention of contesting the will?"

"Contesting it! Good heavens, no."

Amesbury said — I know he's a vestryman of the church that was Milly's — "You're a Christian gentleman, sir, an example to us all."

Dad looked from Amesbury to me and back again, with an expression that asked, "What's the fuss about?" Nine out of ten observers would have labeled the look on his face too good to be true.

"With regard to your immediate expenses," Amesbury said, "as I told you, a spouse has rights, and I'll arrange that for the time being you be paid an income from the estate. I suggest . . ." He mentioned a monthly sum, the matter of probate was discussed, and the little meeting ended.

On the way out Amesbury saw to it that Dad was way-laid by a chatty secretary. "A detail," he said, taking me aside. "About your father and his car. I pass him often on the road, and I know he's a careful driver. But at his age any-thing can happen. I had one friend here locally who was so worried about his old dad's continuing to drive and yet didn't want to be the one to ask him to stop, that he re-ported him anonymously to the state police as being a public danger due to failing eyesight. They called the old man in for an examination and did take away his driver's license."

"I have similar feelings, but I'd hope to handle the situation differently."

"You probably won't have to handle it at all — this is my point — if you can just keep him from buying another car. Because it turns out the present car isn't his. Miss Kirkup mentioned it on the telephone. It seems that when he and your stepmother married he brought his own car with him, like the principal he spoke of, and like the principal he used it till it wore out. Just about that time Mrs. Arnold stopped driving her Buick due to failing health, so he took to driving it, and is still driving it. They never changed the registration, though, and it's still in her name. Miss Kirkup pointed out that consequently the Buick is part of the 'contents of High-lawn' that should be made available to her and her sister 'at everybody's earliest convenience.'" Amesbury made a face. "Not nice. But at least it may make it easier for you to get him away from the wheel. After probate, when the car goes to New Jersey, we can probably arrange for a local driving service of some kind."

"You know he and my stepmother drove to Mexico a few

years ago. They had a lot of close shaves down there, and ever since he's been saying that he 'expects to meet St. Peter on the road.' "

"Another reason to hasten probate. We'll see to it that the Misses Kirkup beat St. Peter to the draw."

Highlawn, Saturday, March 6. Strange to be seeing the old man regularly again — every weekend, now — after the years of keeping at a distance to save him from Milly's tantrums, of coming up just often enough not to seem, at least to myself, and despite the situation, "unnatural," and to keep some watch over the physical side.

I've been running over in my mind the next-to-nothing I know about the courtship. The meeting — chance — my mother and Lejeune in adjacent rooms in the hospital. I saw Milly there once or twice. Both patients died, Lejeune first. Back from Barbados, Dad lived on alone in the house in Greenwich, and after a time began to say, "I was upstate last week and saw Mrs. Lejeune." That was all until he announced imminent marriage. From the beginning there was the intimation, conveyed by Dad awkwardly, tacitly, but quite clearly, that I'd better stay off the reservation. I wasn't asked to the wedding — just the principals and witnesses, I was told, at St. Bridget's in Old Norwich. Soon thereafter, a single phrase of Dad's, uttered in a low, embarrassed voice, set the tone. The phrase, "That might upset things considerably," was in response to a telephone call from me to announce that I'd be weekending nearby and to ask whether a visit would be welcome. The phrase was followed by half-audible whispers between him and Milly and was then amended to an invitation to "drop in Saturday for cocktails." That set the pattern. A few times a year I dropped in Saturday for cocktails "since I was in the neighborhood": of course I always telephoned from New York first. The visits were stiff little affairs. The only one of them at all different from the rest was marked by an outburst in Milly's cracked voice (how did my father stand that voice — the most strident deaf-woman's voice I ever heard?), apparently set off by a mixture stronger than usual: "I was my parents' only child, a spoiled brat from the cradle; and I was Bert Lejeune's only child, spoiled likewise; I have always been spoiled, and I count on being spoiled till my dying day." Is that sufficient explanation of the tantrums that occurred whenever Dad's attention threatened to be diverted from her even briefly? (So far as I can see, there was never anything "personal" about her antagonism to me.) If so, it seems to me a reason as dull as it is unpleasant. I don't see, though, that it can possibly explain the crazy will. More interesting to me, naturally, is my father's case: his longtime turning of the other cheek seems to have escalated in old age to a dedicated masochism.

With the private consent of the local judge, Highlawn has already, before probate, been put on the market. Dad refuses to rent — will only sell. Clear title for a very prompt purchaser could be delayed by the normal probate processes, but this way a little time can perhaps be gained. The Misses Kirkup, however, have been told that the formalities of probate are an absolute prerequisite to their acquisition of the "entire contents."

East 61st Street, Monday, March 15. Yesterday at Highlawn I invited Dad to fly to Rome for a week.

"*Rome? You* want *me* to come to *Rome?*"

"Yes, you know I go to Italy every once in a while. Wouldn't you like to come along?"

"Of course I would, but . . ."

"Then let's go. You could leave in ten days or so, couldn't you? To see the Pope? There'll be a big thing going in St. Peter's."

"Would he see me? Am I really worthy to see him? Why am I so favored? Why does God shower me with his goodness?"

After a moment he went upstairs and stayed there awhile. If I had followed, wouldn't I probably have found him thanking the source — the Source — of this new favor?

East 61st Street. March 17. As I told Dad, it's a special ceremony about to take place in Rome that gave me the idea of our going. Something he should see — the beatification of the Ohio-born founder of an order of nuns, who may become the first North American saint. St. Peter's will be jammed, tickets are essential, and I suggested that he ask Father Healy to help us take the first steps to get them. Telephone call this evening:

"You've certainly let me make a fool of myself."

"How come?"

"I asked Father Healy about tickets to St. Peter's, and his answer was what I should have foreseen. 'Tickets? Who needs tickets to enter a Catholic church?' "

"Didn't you tell him about the Beatification?"

"I told him that you seemed to think we'd need tickets to St. Peter's. He asked where you got the idea that anybody had to pay to enter the house of God. 'Send Ed to me,' he said. 'I'll sell him some tickets — tickets for the car raffle we're having right here for St. Bridget's roof. The books came in today.' I told him I'd take two books — one as usual and one as penance."

"For the Beatification ceremony there are five thousand tickets, all free. It's to limit the crowds that will be trying to get in. I have a newspaper article about it in front of me. The tickets come in eight different colors — red, orange, yellow, green, blue, purple, pink, and white. Each color indicates a different part of the church. If we don't get tickets we don't stand a chance."

"Father Healy would have every reason to be annoyed if I approached him again."

"Don't think of it. I'll attend to it elsewhere."

Next day. My turn to feel foolish in the matter of the tickets. When I told Bill Maguire in the office that I'd tried to begin with a parish priest, he laughed, called a friend in the cardinal's office, and within an hour a messenger arrived with a letter on Archdiocese stationery recommending me to a monsignor, staying at the Excelsior in Rome, who is in charge of distributing Beatification tickets to Americans.

Called Dad. "The ticket problem is solved."

"Faith moves mountains."

Sat for a moment trying to figure that one out. *Whose* faith solved the ticket problem? Apparently inescapable answer: his on whom God bestowed the favor of an invitation to Rome?

The Trip to Rome

In Rome with my father. Grand Hotel Obelisco. Monday, March 29.

No sign at first, this morning, that Dad had been impressed by the all-night transatlantic flight that was his air baptism. He awoke when the lights were turned on for breakfast and remarked that he had always slept well on buses — reminded me that he'd traveled in them all over the Midwest during the thirties when the company he was working for suppressed its salesmen's cars. (Painful feelings aroused in me by that recollection. Did we, my mother and I, appreciate how grueling his life must have been then, bussing from town to town winter and summer, selling a line of tools for a pittance and a commission? She must have, but I'm afraid I didn't. I was in college, paying only part of my way, depending on him for the rest — which he did not give very cheerfully, it relieves me a bit to recall.)

Conspicuous in the sunshine on the Fiumicino airfield as we deplaned was a pair of mounted carabinieri, smart in their black uniforms with gleaming silvery swords. Brilliant also, a mixed group of passengers from an Air India jet nearby — men and women in robes and saris, turbans and bright caps. It was toward them that the two policemen were riding slowly out across the field. While our American stewardess gathered her drab flock together on the concrete Dad stared at the carabinieri. "Nifty ponies," he said — his first words in Latium. "Do you sometimes wonder as I do that President Johnson isn't criticized for riding what is essentially a woman's horse? That Tennessee walking horse of his is effortless to ride — it has a very smooth, even gait, puts only one foot on the ground at a time. They used to be the horses ridden by farm women, carrying baskets of eggs to market, or even pails of milk. But it's a strange mount for an executive."

We were delayed for some reason, and as we approached the terminal entrance the Afro-Orientals were already there, the attendant carabinieri like twin bodyguards. Come to welcome them was a group of fellow nationals in silks and printed cottons — tatooings, cheek-scars, red forehead-spots, kohl-ringed eyes; the two groups melded with much fluttering of saris, salaaming, placing of hands to head and heart. At the center, one potentate accepted particularly deep bows: the presence of the carabinieri hinted at something ambassadorial. "What's the expression?" Dad asked. "'Pomp and circumstance?'" We had another wait as they passed in ahead of us. Now we could see standing beside the entrance another group, come to greet a venerable RC churchman in black with a cerise vest flanked by aides wearing a little less cerise; he was extending his hand to his genuflecting welcomers, as one by one they kissed his ring. My father doffed his hat and hesitated, but we were borne in through the door. Just inside stood a young priest, eagerly scanning the faces of our party. Off came Dad's hat again, and this time he stepped out of line. "Father, may I have your blessing?"

The crew-cut youth looked startled, then embarrassed. He blushed, collected himself. "Oh, sure thing, sir"; and as the old gentleman bowed his head before him he raised his hand and moved his lips.

"Thank you, Father."

"OK, sir. Bye now."

"Did you hear that perfect English?" Dad marveled. "He must be a missionary. The *Catholic Transcript* has been running articles on the terrific language-training job the Church does on missionaries. What was the red trimming on his gown? Is he monsignor, as young as that?"

"Hi, Mom! Great to see yuh! Welcome to th' Eternal City!"

But by then the happy voice of the youngster wearing the colors of the American Seminary was too far behind for Dad to hear it.

After passport control and customs, out at the taxi rank, Dad pointed. "Look — a horse van." He knew why it was there. "The police stables must be rather distant. Shows good sense not to make a valuable horse walk far on the hard road-surfaces we have today. On second thought" — we were in our taxi now — "I take back what I said about the president's horse being a woman's horse. That was uncharitable. Plenty of country preachers, with their churches miles apart, used to ride those Tennessee walkers. I read that somewhere. Such a horse can go fifty miles a day and be ready to do the same the next day. If an ordinary horse walks fifty miles in a day he'll want a day's rest. Nowadays, of course . . . That horse van is certainly a sign of changed times."

He kept talking — a kind of jag, mostly about horses and roads; quite unlike him to be so garrulous. It took me a while to realize that it was excitement about the trip by plane that was betraying itself in this talk of older ways of travel. When we began to pass the ruined columns and arcades of Ostia Antica, I interrupted. "If you'll look across that field to the left, Dad, you'll see a hard-surfaced road that goes back to the Caesars."

" 'Friends, Romans, countrymen!' *That's* a speech I'll never forget. Did I ever tell you about the time I was sitting with Milly in the first row of one of those hard-seated summer theatres she liked to go to, and the sneeze I absolutely couldn't hold back? The actor had stepped to the front of the stage and was just starting it — he was only a few feet away. 'Friends, Romans . . .' — *ker-choo!* I wasn't popular with him, I can tell you. Or with Milly either, God rest her soul."

He talked most of the way into the city; then, when I pointed to St. Peter's dome, he raised his hat and grew quiet.

As I write (5 P.M.) he's sleeping in his room.

Rome. Next day. Last night at dinner he said he felt rested and up to a little walk. From the windows of the roof restaurant of the hotel we saw the full moon, and he asked whether we could visit the Colosseum: he had always heard that it was "quite a sight by moonlight." We got into a taxi, and at the Colosseum I asked the driver to wait, both because the night was chill with a damp that caught at one's throat, and because I wasn't sure what we were going to find. (I remembered Jack W. telling me of taking Dr. Kinsey into the Colosseum at night as one of a series of visits to the more notorious Roman centers of "activity.") Inside, the memorial cross to the martyrs in the center was illuminated, dimming the view of the tiers of seats on the far side. Sure enough, I saw at once that despite the presence of a pair of carabinieri the paths were being put to busy use as an all-male promenade; stares both furtive and bold were being exchanged, and couples were constantly disappearing into or emerging from the unlit, cavelike alcoves along the arc: within them there was the occasional glow of a cigarette or the flame of a match. I made Dad turn up his coat collar. "I certainly admire the fortitude of these Romans, coming out to worship in such a chill," he said. "God forgive me, I'm too cold to say a prayer at the foot of the Cross. I suppose those little rooms off to the side are chapels?" I said they were, "sort of," but too damp for him to enter.

We didn't stay long. The bar in the vaulted entrance-corridor was open, and I ordered brandies. The barman reminded me with solemn face that by law, out of respect for the sacred character of the Colosseum, only soft drinks were dispensed. Dad accepted that as "a very suitable regulation," but when I showed a banknote and the brandy bottle came out from a cupboard, he accepted that too and drained his glass. As we walked toward our taxi there was the sound of a police whistle from within, a man dashed out past us, and then a second. Both disappeared into the night. Dad gave a smile. "Dago stuff, I guess? Vendetta? I keep forgetting we're in the land of the stiletto."

Back at the hotel he pronounced the excursion "inspiring." May our whole week go as well.

This morning I put Dad on one of the sightseeing buses that pick up customers at the various hotels and take them on the tourist circuit that includes the Villa Borghese, and went off myself to the Excelsior and got our St. Peter's tickets. Back at the Obelisco at noon to meet the returning bus; but no one descended from it. The tour guide in the bus saw me waiting and called out: "You're the son? You look like him," and said that he had had the driver stop at the Obelisco only to report the loss of the "*anziano*" who had boarded the bus there. People were always getting back onto the wrong "Pullman" when a whole fleet was parked together here or there, he said. "If I hadn't remembered him as being so very *anziano* and a probable cause of worry to somebody, I wouldn't have bothered. Just wait. He'll turn up." I thanked him and the driver, and they moved on.

Standing at the top of the Spanish Steps across the street from the hotel, not knowing from what direction or in what vehicle the stray might arrive, I was looking toward the façade of the church of Trinita dei Monti, the hotel's immediate neighbor, when I noticed that its central door, which had as usual been shut promptly at twelve, was being opened from within. One of its heavy portals was swinging slowly back, and there in the gradually increasing space was revealed the "*anziano*," pushing it open himself. I ran up the steps as he emerged, and together we pulled the door shut. His bus — he hadn't known until the end that it was the wrong one — had dropped him off at the hotel a little early, and seeing the church open he'd entered and spent some time on his knees. When he rose he found himself locked in. Yes, he had had an interesting tour, he said, when I asked, but he spoke of no particular monument except to mention "that museum where I guess I made my mistake about the bus." The real interest of his morning clearly lay in the necessity he had been under to leave withdrawn, rather than pushed-to as he had found it, the inside bolt on the church door. He spoke about that more than once. "It's sure to give Father Healy a kick. Probably the first time he'll have heard a confession including that particular *faux pas.*" (Dad always pronounces it "*fore paw.*")

"Don't you think it's rather too venial to confess?"

"Don't you know that every little thing can add to one's time in Purgatory?"

Rome. Next day. March 31. Purgatory came up again to-day, in the Catacomb of San Sebastiano.

Including ourselves there were about a dozen waiting when a guide, a stubbly, low-browed Franciscan, emerged from the depths with his earlier party. After pocketing their offerings and trying to interest them in souvenirs — copies of antique crosses and oil lamps in "patined bronze" — he turned to us, and Dad addressed him at once. "Father, may I have your blessing?" The friar looked as amazed as the boy seminarian at the airport: for different reasons, the request must have been of equal rarity in his life. He approached my father curiously. "Mister, you wanta duh bless'?" He was crude enough for an American vaudeville Italian.

"If you'd be so good, Father."

"Cumma dis way."

Dad followed him to a corner of the room, I saw them talking, and saw something pass from one to the other. Then the pupils of the Franciscan's eyes rolled up piously to the vanishing point, he raised his right hand high and made florid blessing-motions. Dad crossed himself, and the two returned to the group. It was hard to credit the blatancy of it, in front of so many of us, all of us staring. Even Dad was aware of appearances. "You mustn't think that Father charged me for the blessing," he murmured to me. "He just asked if I could spare a little to help his sister in Chicago. Her husband walked out on her, and she has several children to support."

After the tour, when I too crossed the Franciscan's palm and rather coldly bade him *arrivederla,* he addressed Dad in Italian in words that I found rather remarkable, and he looked to me to translate them. "What did Father say?" Dad wanted to know.

"Father said," I translated faithfully, "he thinks that you, like himself, are a very good-living man, and that also like himself you won't have to spend more than five hundred years in Purgatory before entering Paradise."

Dad laughed. "Five hundred years! Tell Father he's an optimist!"

The friar understood the last word, and from his look of discomfiture I gathered that for a moment he had the grace to think that his own chances of quick salvation were being questioned — so unaware was he of the unthinkableness of this "good-living man" being sarcastic to the cloth.

"Tell Father," Dad said, "or you tell me and I'll tell him: how do you say in Italian 'Thanks, it's a bargain; I'll buy it'? "

I was impressed by the way he repeated that opinion several times afterwards, when we had left the Franciscan happy again and were outside: "Five hundred years, then Paradise — cheap at the price . . . cheap at the price . . ."

There was an odd little ceremony in the hotel this evening.

At lunchtime all the guests had found notices in their letter boxes announcing that "Signor X, the manager of the Grand Hotel Obelisco, kindly requests the pleasure of your presence at the cocktail party for the opening of the new 'English Bar.' " We didn't attend, but sitting in the lounge after a cup of tea about 6:30 (Dad has adjusted without a murmur to the later hours of Rome) we could look into the lobby and the bar, the latter still empty except for staff, and we saw a gentle-looking old priest, probably from the church next door, arrive with an acolyte. He was greeted not by the manager, but only by the *portiere*, who led him into the bar; there he doffed his round hat, his overcoat, and his jacket, and donned a surplice; the acolyte, also now in surplice, took a silver bowl from a case, filled it with holy water from a flask, and the two proceeded to walk around the room, the acolyte carrying the bowl and the priest dipping and shaking an asperger and murmuring prayers. At one point he walked into a plate-glass door he didn't know was there; one of the bar waiters sprang forward to open it;

35

finding himself out in the hall, the priest looked puzzled; everybody grinned. Then he changed back into his black suit-coat and sat down with the acolyte, also desurpliced, to a platter of canapés and a pair of drinks on the house. Theirs were the first two aperitifs in the newly blessed bar. They were sitting there drinking alone when we went upstairs.

Tomorrow, the Beatification.

Rome, April 1, 196–. He is sleeping now, after spending a total of seven hours at two services in St. Peter's. (I left him from time to time, and spent several of those hours on the roof of the basilica and in a café in the Via della Conciliazione.) The day was a complete success. Never thought I'd see Father Healy's eighty-eight-year-old parishioner standing on a bench inside a church, shouting. Today no wondering was expressed as to whether he was "worthy to see" the Holy Father. The cheering came three times. Once each this morning and this afternoon when the Pope was borne in in the *sedia* and all the extra electric lights in the basilica blazed on like Neapolitan fireworks, and once again, this afternoon, when after Benediction the Pope gave an "audience" — that is, read a message in Italian to the congregation. At the first cheers Dad registered shock and joined in not at all, but by the second session he was participating.

It was while we were standing on our top-row benches this afternoon, amid the cheers following the reading of the message (it was about peace), that we both smelled cigarette smoke. We looked behind us, down into a corridor, where we hadn't previously noticed that the bearers of the *sedia,* a group of young Italians in medieval or Renaissance silks and velvets, were idling the hours between the Pope's arrival and departure. Two or three who were smoking hid their cigarettes as they saw us looking, but none of them interrupted the other pastime they were engaged in. *"Playing cards?"* Dad said incredulously. "In the presence of the Blessed Sacrament?"

I reminded him that following Benediction the Blessed Sac-

36

rament had been put away, and said anyway I suspected that the blasé young porters thought a card game in a corner of St. Peter's as normal as he found bingo in church basements at home. If I had had any doubts as to the success of the day, they would have vanished at his reply: "Normal? With all this taking place a few yards away? *Pimps!*" He flung the word down at them. They couldn't hear it, and probably none would have known its meaning if they had; but one or two of them realized that they were being addressed by a foreigner, and smiled and bowed politely at the probable compliment.

Part of the day's success was due to his being made much of by nuns. He always had a taste for them — two of his own sisters were nuns — and there were hundreds of them on hand today: we learned that many, in the wide white coifs of the American order founded by the lady who was being beatified, had been flown over in groups for the ceremony. During the long wait outside the basilica early this morning, before the doors opened, there was a moment when parts of the crowd of several thousand began to push and shove, and some of the faces around us — just then we were the only men, crushed in a mass of the American nuns — began to look panicky; Dad sensed the uneasiness and began to joke in the corny way I'd often known him to have with nuns: "Sister, that beautiful coif of yours is a big, tempting, white surface, just about half an inch from my fountain pen: wouldn't you like me to autograph it?" and other nonsense that distracted them and had them smiling and answering back. On our benches this afternoon we were beside another lot of American sisters, several of whom had, against all regulations, brought in cameras under their habits and were snapping the Pope. Dad wrote out his address for one or two: "A picture in the mail, please. That's all I ask in return for promising not to report you teen-age smugglers to your Reverend Mother." "What a dad you've got," one of them said to me. "I have the impression he's younger than you are."

In the taxi on the way back to the hotel, we passed an

illuminated El Al signboard: NOW SEE THE HOLY LAND — as it were, "You've read the book, now see the movie." Dad's interpretation of the slogan was another tribute to the success of the day: "To think that I really *have* seen it!" And at dinner in the roof-restaurant he raised his wineglass to the floodlit dome of St. Peter's that glowed against the sky: "To my pal."

"Do you mean St. Peter's, because you've got to know it so well, or His Holiness himself?"

"Just the whole shebang."

He seemed a little tight — and not on the wine.

New York, Monday, April 5. The day following the ceremony in St. Peter's he did little but rest; then came a day of being driven to a succession of other churches; then we took the westbound plane and landed safely at Kennedy. He wouldn't spend the night with me in New York — had arranged with John Murphy, the Old Norwich taxi man, to meet him at the airport and drive him straight home. Rather excited in the plane about the "probability" that Highlawn had already found a buyer — "I have a feeling it's been snapped up," etc. I gathered that that expectation of quick success was somehow connected with all the blessings he'd been garnering in Rome.

The last day was certainly a blessing-harvest. It was "Father, may I have your blessing?" everywhere we went. In Santa Sabina the blesser was a melancholy Savonarola of a Dominican who asked me Dad's age and when he heard it bade me pass on the news that it was one of which he himself could expect to reach only a fraction: "Six operations so far — my stomach's the size of a watch pocket." Dad shook his head and pursed his lips at my lighthearted, ill-considered suggestion that in this case the blesser seemed to stand in greater need of blessing than the blest: "One thing you'll never understand is religion." In Santa Cecilia a scholarly looking German in glasses and a red-pomponned biretta stared at me as he blessed Dad — I was standing a bit away — and informed me, I couldn't tell whether sternly or compassionately but certainly with intuition, "That goes for you, too." In St. Paul's Without the Walls, a wish — "I hope they put him to bed with a hot water bottle and a toddy" — was expressed concerning a shivering old cardinal in a black fur cape who certainly shouldn't have been allowed, that day, to doff the cape, don gold vestments, and say Vespers in the frigid church: as he tottered out past us into the cloister there was an exchange of glances between him and Dad — they seemed about of an age — and quite without being asked he raised a hand in our direction and moved his lips and his waxy fingers. Best company were the Irish fathers in San Clemente: they could be talked to like nuns. "What would you say, Father, if I were to tell you that my first wife's uncle was named Hagerty and was bishop of Hartford, Connecticut?" "I'd say you didn't need that blessing I'm afther giving you: I know me betters when I see them." "Give our love to your beautiful Connecticut central heating — here the damp's nothing short of pagan."

In the plane, with Highlawn a few hours away, he suddenly spoke of the night I'd seen him open the back door for Father Healy. "We'd got into the habit of doing it that way the last few months. With Milly in the state she was, and often nobody coming to help out Sunday mornings, there were times when I had to miss Mass, and Father Healy has been coming to hear my confession and give me Communion. I might have spared him the trouble by going to him during the week, but Milly was always uneasy when I was out of the house, and wanted to know where I'd been. I don't think I ever told you that when Father used to come in to see me during my sick spell a few years ago Milly wasn't very hospitable to him, so this time it seemed best to make his visits as inconspicuous as possible. Hence the back door. That night you saw him, he was keeping an appointment we'd made before Milly passed on. By then he *could* have come to the front, but it seemed best to keep things as they were, out of respect, you might say, at least for the moment."

"I hadn't realized that Milly was anti-Catholic."

"I wouldn't put it that way. It was a feeling she had about Father Healy."

"What did she dislike about him?"

"It was just a feeling she had."

It was obvious even to one who had seen him as rarely as I that Father Healy was a rough diamond, if diamond he was. My mother used to tell of hearing her "Uncle Bishop," as she called him, lament his inability to put much polish on the Connecticut boys he recruited for the priesthood: Father Healy had been one of them. Milly, who considered beer-drinking fishermen "trashy," could scarcely find him to her taste.

Reflecting on it since, I'm tempted to interpret Dad's end-of-trip confidences about Father Healy as his peculiar way of thanking me for the week in Rome, somewhat as his excitement about the flight *to* Rome had expressed itself only in a talking-jag about horses. Certainly the confidences were addressed more directly to me than the overt thanks that he offered as we separated: "It was wonderful. Praise God from whom all blessings flow."

The Sale

Highlawn, June 30. Two months now since Rome, and Dad is disappointed and puzzled by what he considers the overly protracted nonsale of Highlawn.

I've been coming up every other weekend or so, and sometimes one of the men or women real estate agents brings around a prospective buyer, but no luck so far. Dad complains about the agents' "inactivity." Highlawn is imposing, perhaps too imposing for most modern house-hunters, standing at the top of a steep drive, its slate mansard roof crowning the two lofty stories and the wrought iron of the veranda, all painted glossy white. One of the women agents told me that its period is a disadvantage: "Everything Victorian's taken a nose dive," she confided. Besides, "Country properties aren't moving." Today I could buy any one of fifty houses in Old Norwich, she told me: "Everybody wants to sell, and your dad's asking price of fifty is not realistic." One young couple, especially the wife, was much taken with Highlawn until it occurred to the husband to ask whether the drive wasn't a nuisance in winter. "Not in the least," Dad replied. "Tommy Rumbold's the most reliable young fellow in the community, and he's under permanent orders to salt this drive at the slightest snowfall or sign of ice."

"So it *is* a nuisance," the young husband said, and he took his wife away. Dad told me later that that couple had bought what he described as "an old clapboard shed dolled up for sale by a group of the agents — I guess those youngsters fell for the fancy bathrooms and the Greenwich Village shade of pink the place has been painted." He spoke with a kind of pained scorn, as though he were seeing some cheap-jack phony being preferred to an estimable friend. I sympathize with him: Highlawn is authentic and handsome, and Dad has shown me a dozen details of its splendid construction: each of its many paneled doors is still perfectly joined, after a hundred years or so.

East 61st Street. Monday, June 14. Something of an eye-opener at Highlawn yesterday.

When Dad returns after driving to Sunday Vespers, which he is now free to attend, Father Healy is sometimes with him. Apparently because he has observed that Dad and I get along "harmoniously," as Dad would put it, that even so devout a father puts up with so backsliding a son, he has taken to including me in his brand of cordiality: "Hi there, Ed, you old city slicker! Bet you're glad to get away from New York — *I* wouldn't live there if you paid me." Whiskey sours are made, and the three of us sit around the fire, forming a cocktail trio different in only a third of its membership from the Milly-Dad-and-me trios of the past. Dad obviously feels much freer to enjoy these, and for him the talk is easier. Instead of listening silently while Milly disapproves of the Metropolitan

Museum's latest line of Christmas cards, he holds his own in the conversational replaying of the latest baseball games that he and Father Healy watched on television; and Father Healy's confidences concerning summer parishioners — "Are they loaded! Humble Oil on her side, for one thing," — bring in reply "I hear they're wonderful people," or "I hope they're generous to St. Bridget's." If Dad leaves the room, Father Healy is apt to lean over and nudge me with an elbow: "What a great old boy that is!" or "Your dad's the greatest!" And after Father Healy's departure Dad has his own set piece: "There's a man who's seen life in the raw. You know when he was curate in Danbury his duties included being prison chaplain."

Anyway, yesterday the set piece was followed by something more: 'Did I ever tell you about Father's refusing to marry us?"

This was news. "But he did marry you, didn't he?"

"He did eventually, after he was ordered to. Milly consented readily enough to be married by a priest — she knew that for me it was the only thing — but when we first went to Father Healy he turned us down flat. Did I never tell you this?"

He knew quite well, I'm sure, that he hadn't.

"He said that according to the book the choice of whether or not to perform a mixed marriage is up to the individual priest, and that he'd never done it and never would do it, and that we'd have to go elsewhere. I was all for Greenwich — I knew any of my friends at St. Mary's would marry us like a shot — but Milly was on her high horse by then and said she'd been insulted and wasn't going to 'traipse around from priest to priest.' So I telephoned the diocesan office for advice. I don't know anybody there anymore — you know they've partitioned the old diocese and made all kinds of changes — but as luck had it Monsignor Mongan happened to be on hand that day, even though he's retired, and I knew God was being good to me again. Monsignor said he'd have somebody give Father Healy a telephone call: I gather they find him a little balky at times. Monsignor seemed to think it quite a joke, especially considering Mother's connection with the old bishop. He told me to reapply to Father Healy in a week. I did — I practically had to drag Milly to the rectory — and this time he was quite gracious. He said yes, he'd give us the sacrament of matrimony, and furthermore, considering Milly's time of life, he'd spare her the usual instruction concerning possible children. He has quite a sense of humor, you know. She let him tie the knot, but I'm afraid she found his reference to her age superfluous."

For once I was too heated to keep quiet. "Dad, you know that you yourself would have recognized it as oafishness in anybody else, and would have resented it too."

"Father Healy's a man's man, the foursquare type. Milly, God rest her soul, was a great one for holding a grudge. I can't stand being on bad terms with people. If I'd followed her lead, Father and I wouldn't be the pals we are now." And he added, mild as usual when on this subject with me: "Ed, I wish you'd just remind yourself every once in a while that you simply don't understand religion."

I left soon after that, and all the way to the city memories long soothingly quiescent kept boiling up so angrily that at times I had to remind myself to watch the road. Milly had had to open her door, during my father's illness, to the "man's man" who had refused her and chaffed her; and during *her* illness he had been let into her house repeatedly — all of it done in perfect disregard of her feelings. But what was that, in comparison with the disregard shown — and for how many years! — to another woman, herself born into the Church but trying to make life in this world something more than merely decent for the three of us, all the time living with what she must have soon come to recognize as a case of rampant preoccupation with the "salvation of one's immortal soul." Isn't that particular form of gluttony perhaps a sin, in the calendar of sins, with a name of its own? "Five hundred years of Purgatory — then Paradise"; "Every little thing can add to one's time in Purgatory": wasn't that what had always motivated everything, been responsible for the drudgery, the absence of servants, the rarity of outings and new clothes, pinched lips when Mother or I spoke of college and of college bills, the limited friendships and acquaintances, the moves until nearly the end from one ramshackle rented house to another, with meanwhile the offerings continuing unabated, week after week, with "Special Collections" calling for special contributions, and little gifts throughout the year to convent and rectory, with "Remember me in your prayers" always understood as part of the package? It can only have been at additional cost to herself, a dimming of her own light, that she stifled her protests, keeping things quiet as far as my young ears were concerned; yet everything was so plain to me, so faultlessly picked up by a child's antennae, that there came into being almost imperceptibly the condition that Dad still today calls my "nonunderstanding of religion." In fact, with me religion in his sense never stood a chance; all I could see was the religiosity, and I never even turned my back on it — merely avoided it. The effect on my mother was graver: the very religion of her youth was soured — and of this my father, always hardworking, always considerate of her in other ways, went on in sublime, blind unawareness. Her few words about it during her last illness astounded me — but only, I think, because she was finally uttering them: the condition they articulated had long been a silent part of both of us: "If I ask for a priest, don't be taken in: I'll be doing it for his sake."

(*Reminder:* it's one thing to recall the past, and another to surrender to it, let it take over. Desist! In those last lines I have broken no new ground, set down nothing new, nothing I haven't long known. The chief thing: Dad is eighty-eight — to be seen through to the end.)

However, there's this: after a cocktail a bit too strong, Milly described herself one Saturday afternoon as one who had always been a spoiled brat. Born into comfort, she meant, and pampered ever since. Hadn't someone else in the room at that moment been pampered too, in different ways? And what about Milly's will? Even if its chief purpose had really been the determination to keep a priest's housekeeper from becoming the mistress of Highlawn, that begins to seem if no more amiable at least less surprising in the light of my father's confidences. And was there perhaps more to it than that?

East 61st Street. June 27. Unexpectedly quick answer to the question ending the last entry.

Today, Highlawn for Sunday dinner only, because there's a guest in residence — Aunt Anna, come for a few days' visit to her brother in this house where, though I'm sure she knows nothing of the story, she'll never be mistress.

Dad was speculating as to where he might live after leaving Highlawn. (It's still on the market.) He's getting a little careless in what he lets fall: someone should warn him that his revelations are showing.

"As I made clear to Milly," he said, "it's a matter of indifference to me where I spend my last days. There's something I don't think I ever told you." (He's using that phrase more and more often.) "About the time Mother died and I was alone, I got in the mail an appeal from a hostel in Alabama, run by a very small community of monks who devote themselves entirely to old men who are poor and alone in the world. I recognized that coming just then it was more a message than a mere coincidence, and sent a contribution and kept it up. Then Milly and I married and I moved here. When she and I were driving to Mexico I made it a point to turn inland off the Gulf Highway and go call on the brothers — I knew some of their names by this time, from correspondence. They welcomed me with open arms. What a marvelous job they do there on a shoestring! The poverty! Rows of old men, Negroes mostly, on straw pallets! Stove heat! Of course I shook hands with them all and chatted with those that could be chatted with. If I say so myself, my visit made it a red-letter day for them, inmates *and* brothers. Very dreary back-country. They don't see many strange faces."

After a pause he went on. "I never fully understood Milly's

reaction to that hostel. First of all she hadn't much appreciated interrupting the nice pleasure drive along the Gulf, and then she couldn't take the poverty of the place. After one look she wouldn't even accept the cup of coffee the brothers offered — ran back out and waited for me in the car. When I rejoined her I said something like 'Well, that's one place that will always have room for me.' Boy — did that turn out to be a *fore paw*. She went wild. She let out a one-word rocket: '*Blackmail!*' Of course I couldn't let her think that, and it was then and there I made clear to her that it was a matter of indifference to me where my last days might be spent, and that she was under no obligation whatever to provide for me."

He paused again. "One thing *was* my fault," he said. "I'd been too open with Milly. When the house in Greenwich was sold I naturally wanted to make an offering of at least a tithe of the proceeds, and I felt nobody could make better use of it than the brothers at the Alabama hostel. And when I told Milly about the small capital I had, I gave her the complete figures, specifying the sale price of the house minus the tithe to Alabama. I wish I hadn't. Because as it happened, it was shortly after our visit to Alabama that my money ran out, and one day, discussing the situation, Milly let slip something about charity beginning at home. I have a feeling she was referring to the tithe, and perhaps to certain other contributions I'd been continuing to make, meaning that if I hadn't given them I'd still have a few thousand dollars in the bank — enough to see me through, perhaps. I assured her then again that she was under no obligation to provide for me."

Such was that tale. It ended rather abruptly, particularly since I could think of no "harmonious" comment to make.

As I reflected on it, I realized that it must have been about then — after my father's money ran out and shortly before she fell ill — that Milly did make provision for him, in the will that involved the sale of Highlawn in order to get cash. Cash with which he could . . . I almost grinned as I imagined how Milly herself, in her cracked, querulous voice, might have furnished the next words: ". . . do as he damn-well pleased," perhaps? Somehow I felt like giving Milly a bit of a cheer.

I think that most of Dad's revelations about the hostel were lost on Aunt Anna, who sat quietly at table with us. She's frail, tottery, not too responsive. Much of the time she holds her head with both hands: she says it's the only way she can keep it from "spinning off." But suddenly she said to Dad: "Maybe you and I could take a little apartment together somewhere." So far as I know, she's never had a home of her own, having gone straight from her room in the rectory to the convent where she boards now. "I could manage part of the furniture, Joe, and . . ." It sounded like the plea of a twenty-year-old for her own establishment, whereas Anna is eighty-six or so to my father's eighty-eight.

"Much too late for that kind of pipe dream," Dad said. "We'd both better start thinking about old-age homes. What do you hear about St. Timothy's in New Britain?"

Anna caught at that as next best. "I hear it's lovely. If you go there I'll go too."

"You will?" Dad sounded as though he thought she was having another pipe dream, and in fact he explained to me later that the rates at St. Timothy's and other such places were "pretty steep" and that Anna was "deluding herself in thinking she could swing it."

I may be naïve, but I'm sure Milly was partly wrong in her diagnosis of "*Blackmail!*" I don't believe that Dad's words about being sure of a welcome at the hostel were *pure* blackmail, hard though his unconscious may have been working to make them so. Because: although of course he won't spend his last days at the hostel, and may quite well spend them at expensive St. Timothy's (and Milly's "charity begins at home" doesn't promise to sway him toward helping Aunt Anna go there with him: would he in fact have asked her to live with him at Highlawn had he been able to?), still I'm sure that if fate were, after all, to reduce him to the hostel, he'd stoically accept the verdict, and — this certainly — enjoy being what he would equally certainly become — the brothers' best-loved inmate.

Highlawn. Saturday, July 11.
THE BLESSING OF A HOUSE
Stole — Color of the Day.
The Priest, vested in Surplice and Stole, says:
Our help is in the name of the Lord.
R. Who hath made heaven and earth.
V. The Lord be with you.
R. And with thy spirit.
Let us pray.

O Heavenly Father, almighty God, we humbly beseech Thee to bless † and sanctify † this house and all who dwell therein and everything else in it, and do Thou vouchsafe to fill it with all good things: grant to them, O Lord! the abundance of heavenly blessings and from the richness of the earth every substance necessary for life, and finally direct their desires to the fruits of Thy mercy. At our entrance, therefore, deign to bless † and sanctify † this house as Thou didst deign to bless the house of Abraham, of Isaac, and of Jacob; and may the Angels of Thy light dwell within the walls of this house; and may they protect it and those who dwell within. Through Christ our Lord.

R. Amen
The Priest then SPRINKLES the house with HOLY WATER.

I've copied out the above from Dad's English-language missal. As I listened to it this morning from the porch, it was a little different. Father Healy read it in Latin, and he made the responses himself, being alone, without acolyte, unlike the priest who blessed the hotel bar in Rome. Dad told me that the other day, when he received in the mail a few rather blurred snapshots of the Papal Benediction in St. Peter's, sent him with a note by one of the nuns with the smuggled cameras, he recalled that bar-blessing along with other Roman details, and that recollection suddenly made him realize what Highlawn lacked. "What with it staying unsold for so long, I'd begun to think there must be a curse on it. Then it occurred to me it's the only unblessed house I've ever lived in in my life." He was nervous last night about the impending ceremony. "Keep out of the way, if you don't mind. Above all, don't attempt to have any conversation with Father, as he may be carrying the Blessed Sacrament. At least he'll have it in the car. He told me he'd be coming from giving Communion to one of the Doran girls, who's quite low."

Father Healy arrived about nine, and as he got out of his car I saw that he was already wearing a white stole over his ordinary clothes. He didn't change to a surplice, Dad says. He said the prayer in the living room, then went upstairs. It was all over in about ten minutes, and he came out of the house alone and drove off.

"Didn't you offer him a drink, Dad, like the barman in Rome?"

"With the Blessed Sacrament waiting to go back to the sanctuary? Certainly not."

Blessed Sacrament or not, I'd noticed that Father Healy removed his stole and lit a cigarette as he reentered his car.

"There's more to Highlawn than just the house, Dad. Shouldn't the garden have been blessed, too?"

"I didn't feel it was necessary."

It's true that he always had the greenest of thumbs, and nowadays the flowers and vegetables still flourish splendidly unblessed, under Tommy Rumbold.

"What about the barn?"

"Barns are blessed when there's livestock or produce in them. In my barn there's only the Buick. I had that blessed several years ago — Milly never knew."

East 61st Street. Sunday night, July 19. The immediate sale of Highlawn, twenty-four hours after the blessing, has been accompanied by certain details of which one I hope will always remain unknown to my father.

The entire thing has put him into a state of decidedly holy excitement. What happened was that a local real estate agent named John Quinn, who of all the agents was the one about whose "inactivity" my father had most complained, came in with his wife, "out of the blue," my father told me on the phone, and made an offer — low, but all cash. "Ever since you put Highlawn on the market we've been coveting it," my father reported him as saying. "Mrs. Quinn's mother is getting on, and we want to take her in with us and need a little more room. But only when we found a buyer for our own house did it become possible." Quinn made his offer the day after the blessing. His own house had been sold the day *of* the blessing. My father sought out Father Healy at once to tell him the news. "Two houses sold by your single blessing, Father!" Father Healy seemed "staggered." He gave Dad "a stupefied look," was "speechless for a couple of seconds," and then said in a "gulping voice," "Joe, your faith is certainly extraordinary." I gathered that the priest didn't know whether to give the major share of the credit to his own powers, or to Dad's remarkable state of grace.

I find the double sale not too surprising, not too different from many things in the past. After all, whenever my mother lacked piano pupils (of course she wouldn't have had to give lessons if it hadn't been for Dad's donations) it was Dad's prayers to St. Cecilia that brought her new ones; St. Anthony was forever finding lost pocketknives, watches, and rings; and St. Joseph, the carpenter, once stretched a board almost a quarter of an inch, to fit into a set of shelves Dad was making at his workbench. For Dad, the event is an occasion not only for thanksgiving, but also for a rousing *mea culpa* — expressed to me as well as, no doubt, in the confessional. "When I think of how unjustly I spoke about John Quinn, practically accusing him of being a ne'er-do-well, when all the time he was concentrating on selling his own

place, with Highlawn in mind! What does the Gospel say —
'The greatest of these is charity'?"

This morning while Dad was at Mass and I was reading the
New York Times on the porch, a car came up the drive and
a youngish man got out and introduced himself as John Quinn.
He must have heard from Dad that I'd be there, and timed
his visit carefully: it was I whom he wanted to see. He told
me what a grand old man my father was — "a real saint, we
think him up here" — and then asked me: "Ed, do you think
your dad really wants to sell this house?"

"I know he does, John." (First names come *à l'américaine*
in Old Norwich.)

"You don't think that after we sign the deed its validity
could be questioned for any reason?"

"What's on your mind, John?"

Quinn hemmed and hawed a little before plunging ahead.
"Ed, let me tell you in confidence what happened. That
morning Mrs. Quinn and I called on your father, I didn't
have to ask him how much he wanted for his house. I knew
already, because the house was listed with me along with the
other agents. I just laid my cards on the table. I mean I told
him how much I was willing to pay — how much I *could*
pay. What I offered was quite a little less than he was asking,
but I offered it all in cash. He thought for a moment and
mentioned a figure a bit higher — the price I thought he'd
fix on, frankly. I agreed, and we shook hands. It was a transaction of the rarest, pleasantest kind — took about three minutes
in all. I gave him my deposit check and he said let's drink on
it. He asked us what we'd like and suggested whiskey sours
and we said fine. He went out to the kitchen to mix them.
He was gone a long time, so very long that we looked at each
other and wondered what was going on. There wasn't a
sound to be heard. Finally Mrs. Quinn said she'd better go
out and see if she could help. In a minute she came tiptoeing
back. She whispered to me that your father was on his knees
in the kitchen, crying. The tears were wet on his face, she

said, and his lips were moving. He hadn't noticed her come in or go out. We sat there and waited, and eventually we heard water running, and some tinkling, and finally he came in with the tray of drinks and snacks, his normal cheerful self. No one would know he'd been through anything. Now Ed, what we're wondering, frankly, is, if he's as strongly attached to the house as that seems to indicate, attached to Mrs. Arnold's memory and all that — which, frankly, between us, man to man, surprises me — if it's such a terrible wrench to sell, why, perhaps at the last minute he might . . ."

"No, no, John. Of course he misses my stepmother. But he won't back out. He's happy to sell."

"Ed, I've got to be brutally frank. Mrs. Quinn and I are good Catholics, and we recognize prayer when we see it. But your father's well into his eighties. When people in their eighties start to cry, even if it's only in mourning for a loved one, that's often the beginning of what's known as senility. It's an ugly word, but we've all got to face it. Now a contract made with a person known to be senile . . ."

Was Quinn forgetting that just a few minutes earlier he had called my father "a real saint"? When it came to contracts, apparently the tears of a saint were disquietingly like something else. But all I said was that Dad was certainly not senile, that if Quinn were really worried he could get a professional opinion from Dr. Bergin or the attorney Amesbury, and that anyway I would personally guarantee the contract. I didn't think I should reveal the true nature of the tears. In fact I wasn't sure that I knew it myself. "Thanksgiving," of course. But thanksgiving can be so many things. Among them, joy caused by recognition and confirmation of one's own worthiness, no? A kind of sublime content, exalted self-satisfaction? Relief at receiving an unmistakable message from on high that one has been a "good-living man" whose time in Purgatory will be minimal?

The closing will probably be in two or three weeks. Probate is being speeded up and will be finished about then; title search is little more than a formality, Highlawn being, as

Amesbury puts it, "neat and clean in all respects." Dad is to be able to stay in the house a month after closing. Then — where? He seems to have given that question no further consideration. All his thoughts are on the marvelous results of the blessing.

Query: is it really kosher to have a house blessed in order to get rid of it?

Highlawn. Three weeks later. Sunday, August 9. Dad and I have had Words.

To have Words with an eighty-eight-year-old parent about money sounds on the face of it about as low as one can get, and it's left me feeling mean. What cost me my temper was his telling me yesterday, in a matter-of-fact way, that out of the sale price of Highlawn — he hasn't revealed what it is, and I haven't asked: probably somewhere in the thirties — he plans to give ten thousand dollars in contributions. Five thousand to Father Healy "because he made it all possible," and five to his favorite order of missionary fathers: "They're doing a wonderful job in Guatemala, counteracting communist atheism among the Indians: the money will buy them a jeep they badly need."

"Are you serious?"

"Perfectly serious."

"But what about yourself? You're in wonderfully good shape; you may well live to be a hundred — you'll need your money to live on."

"I have confidence."

"Confidence in what? In *Whom?*" This came out as a sneer. I could hear myself put the sarcastic capital on *Whom.* It's me that my father has confidence in, and he knows it, and he's perfectly right to have that confidence. Why does he have to pretend it's Someone Else? Even before the sound of the capital letter died away I awaited the answer that didn't fail to come:

"You've never understood religion."

The excitements of this past fortnight beginning with the

blessing have made him bellicose, and straightaway he de-
livered another punch: "Also, I'm going to leave a certain
sum of money in a sealed, stamped, addressed envelope that
I'll ask you to put in the mail after my death. It's for a
special intention." I gave him a cold look, and then he really
let me have it: "It's for prayers that will insure my meeting
up with Mother in the other world more quickly than would
otherwise be the case."

I got up and walked away. I told myself that it was my
fault, that I might not have had to hear that last part if I'd
kept cool about the first; if when he spoke of "confidence"
I'd just said that of course he could have confidence, perfect
confidence, in *me*. I found myself wondering whether his
first, matter-of-fact-sounding announcement of the ten thousand was in itself a mark of confidence in me. Confidence
that after all these recent "harmonious" months I could be
counted on finally to "understand." Or was it a baiting, more
or less unconscious?

Anyway, it greatly marred the closing, which we both
attended a few hours later and which should have been a
completely joyful event. Amesbury kept looking at us: he
could tell that something was amiss. After Quinn's check was
handed over, and the deed was signed, and the Quinns left
with handshakes all round, Dad said in a strange voice, "Mr.
Amesbury, there's something I wish to say."

"Yes, Mr. Arnold."

"Mr. Amesbury, do you consider me of sound mind?"

It was uncanny: it was impossible that he should have got
wind of the Quinns' worry.

"Certainly, Mr. Arnold."

"Then let me say this. I have been criticized for certain
donations that I intend to make with part of this money that
has changed hands here today. However, though I know
that my son thinks them unjustified, and I suspect that you
would, too, Mr. Amesbury, if I were to detail them to you,
I have justification here" — he touched his forehead with a
forefinger — "for every dollar I intend to give. And I don't

54

think I should be treated roughly, during my last remaining years, for following my only interest."

Amesbury kept an admirably professional deadpan, only his eyes betraying uncertainty. "Why, I'm sure, Mr. Arnold, that everyone would agree that a little judicious sharing is in order on such an occasion. It's not as though you had twelve or fourteen children to provide for, or . . ."

To my chagrin I felt my eyes smarting. "But you do have one son," I said, "and it doesn't give him much pleasure to hear you say that the Church is your only interest."

"He's got you there, Mr. Arnold."

But Dad said nothing.

We both bade Amesbury good-bye, and drove silently back to Highlawn. Later, during the evening that seemed very long and heavy, almost without conversation, I asked him whether he had thought about the future.

"We'll discuss that some other time."

This morning at breakfast I told him I was sorry I had offended him, but couldn't resist adding, "You know you offended me, too."

"I should have known better than to raise certain questions."

He went to Mass, lunch was very quiet, and when he made ready to go to Vespers I held out my hand. He looked startled. "You're driving back earlier than usual?"

"There's someone I have to see." Actually, I preferred not to let myself in for an after-Vespers trio with Father Healy. "I'll call you tonight."

"Well, good-bye, then."

"Good-bye, Dad."

I did call him, just now. We exchanged a few lame remarks; then, as we were about to hang up, something occurred to him. "Oh, did I tell you that Anna passed away?"

He had forgotten to mention it. She died on Friday, the day before our Words and the closing. "What with so many things on my mind it clean left me." He's to drive to the funeral in

Hartford tomorrow. "I imagine there'll be nobody there except me and some of the nuns she's been living with."

"Do you want me to come?"

"Don't think of it. I guess you saw for yourself last month she was falling apart. Well, that's that."

Another day, I might have insisted on joining him in Hartford, or on picking him up in Old Norwich and driving him there. As it was, there was something in his voice that told me I was the last person in the world he'd like to have beside him in church; or, if he wasn't saying that, I imagined it. "We'll talk about it and other things tomorrow night," I said. "I'll call you. Don't let it get you too down."

"OK. Good-bye, then."

"Good-bye. Be careful on the road."

Epilogue

I never spoke with him again.

He reached Hartford all right, attended Anna's funeral Mass, and even drove to the cemetery. On the way back I'm sure he thought he was being as careful as usual, but with "so many things on his mind" — and the funeral now added to them — he apparently wasn't up to it. On the outskirts of Hartford he drove through a red light, a truck hit the Buick, and, as he would have put it, "that was that." They found my name in his billfold and called me at the office.

He didn't know it, but he had just inherited close to a hundred thousand dollars. That was the "residue" of Aunt Anna's estate, after bequests to her nuns and various Catholic charities. It seems that Anna's pastor, the one she kept house for so long, had a flair for the market: he had no funds of his own to invest, but it was his hobby to advise his friends. Anna did everything he told her, and over many years her "portfolio" grew and grew. So Highlawn need never have been sold, after all.

And because of the very conclusive way St. Peter had arranged the meeting on the road — his agent, who worked for a firm of movers in Torrington, and who was unscathed al- though according to the police "badly shaken and upset," got my address from them and sent me a printed "sympathy" card with ("Truckdriver") in parentheses and quotes beneath his signature — there was no Buick for the cousins in New Jersey.

And I have often thought of the triumphant occasion for thanksgiving that Dad missed — the knowledge that his "con- fidence" had been utterly justified.

After Dad's own funeral — he's beside my mother in Green- wich — Amesbury showed me his will, made before the sale, when his cupboard was bare. Whatever there was, was left to me, with the request that I make a few modest donations. Of course what actually came to me included the entire sale price of Highlawn — it turned out to be thirty-five — and naturally I found myself writing out checks for five thousand each to Father Healy and the missionaries. (That latter bit of Dad's generosity may have misfired: just yesterday I read in the *Times* that in Guatemala a group of missionary nuns and priests had defected to the guerrillas, "taking the mission jeep along with them.") I even found the "stamped addressed envelope," not yet sealed, and put something in it to insure that the meet- ing with my mother not be delayed.

Of course much the largest sum that's come to me is Aunt Anna's little fortune that she left to Dad. This I still have: I've seen no good reason to give it away. What would Dad have done with it, I wonder? A hypothetical question — I mean, permanently so: I miss him; but for myself I don't believe he knows I do, and much less that we'll be able to discuss the matter in the future. Despite the circumstantial evidence.

(1970)

The System

I was living near Naples at the time, and was spending the afternoon in the city, doing the antique shops in the Via Costantinopoli. In one of them I found a rather nice Victorian rose lustre plate, but the fifteen-or-so-year-old boy who was the only person in the shop told me that he didn't know the price. He suggested that I come again later, when "the Signora" would have returned.

In another shop, half a block away, I was welcomed by two men, one middle-aged and the other young, the latter wearing a stained black T-shirt over nondescript trousers. Here I saw a pair of white Giustiniani cups and saucers with twisted handles; the price, said the older man, clearly the proprietor, was ten thousand lire. It took only a raising of the eyebrows to reduce this to nine, a smile to bring it to eight, and then, when I shook my head, I was asked to make an offer. I said "Five," and the word was barely uttered when the older man cried *"Venduti!"* and handed the cups and saucers to his assistant for wrapping.

I paid the five thousand lire, the older man offered me a cigarette, and, as the younger proceeded to make my package, I told them I had a question to ask. "I know that in Italy the customer is often expected to make an offer," I said, "but it's not a system that inspires me with confidence. For instance, how do I know that you wouldn't have taken one thousand lire, or even less, for the cups and saucers?"

The older man wagged a finger at me. "Impossible, Signore," he said. "Your question shows you're not a Neapolitan. No Neapolitan would dream of accepting less than half the price he asked. It would make him lose face. Don't you know our expression *'fare una brutta figura'?* We refuse absolutely to put ourselves in that position."

"Even when you really want to make a sale?" I asked. "Be frank with me. I've paid you the five thousand lire. The sale is made — it's over and done with. There's no question of my reneging. Just tell me honestly — how much less would you have taken?"

The finger wagged again. "Not a single lira, Signore. Not in Naples. It's our system. You'll find that every section of Italy has its system, Signore. In Tuscany, where they pride themselves on being proper and stiff-necked, I'm told they come down very, very little. They must miss a lot of sales that way, and it seems to me foolish. In Sicily" — and here the antique dealer's harsh Neapolitan voice took on a harsher, more raucous tone, expressive of scorn — "in Sicily, they will accept anything, *anything*. In Sicily, it's the failure to make a sale that brings loss of face. Is that not contemptible? Here in Naples, we have the golden mean — *il medio d'oro*. A well-thought-out asking price, down fifty percent if we have to, and — *basta!* — the customer takes it or leaves it."

All this time, the conversation had been in Italian. The younger man, making his package, had been following it with intense, wide-eyed interest, occasionally nodding his enthusiastic agreement. Now he spoke. "Signore," he said, ad-

59

dressing me eagerly, "I want you to know that my uncle — this gentleman is my uncle — is telling you the truth. Not a lira less would he have taken, I assure you." Abandoning the package, he stepped toward me and, to my surprise, broke into English — an English that was faulty but no less eager than his Italian. "I have lived in Chicago, sir," he cried. "I understand both systems, the Italian and the American. Listen to what I have to say, sir." He was almost shouting by now, and he began to pluck at his black T-shirt as though it were scratching him. "Ordinarily, I do not wear black when I am at work among antiquities. It is not practical. It stains, and shows the dust, as you see. But at present I am wearing *lutto*, Signore — how do you say '*lutto*' in English?"

I murmured "Mourning," but he did not hear me, so intent was he on rushing ahead with what he had to say. Indeed, by the time I had spoken he had already found a translation of his own. "Loot, Signore. I am in loot for my deceased father, may God rest his soul. And I swear to you on this loot" — the dirty black T-shirt was now grasped with both hands and shaken almost hard enough to tear it from the wearer's body — "on this loot that I wear for my father, that my uncle would not have come down another lira."

What was there to say to that? I inclined my head in a gesture that was half nod of acceptance of his assurances, half bow of condolence for his bereavement. I accepted another cigarette from the uncle, the nephew returned to his wrapping, and for a few moments there was silence among us.

"Not all foreigners observe our system the way you observed it even before I told you it was a system, Signore," the uncle then said to me, again in Italian. "I have had foreigners here who seemed quite unable to grasp the *principle* of the thing. Why, I have had American customers who informed me, before asking a single price, that their friends had told them to 'bargain.' " He used the English word, emphasizing it and making a face as he did so. "Here in Naples, we do not like the sound of that word 'bargain' of yours. It seems to us not very elegant, not very civilized. I am truly sorry for your compatriots who come in announcing their intention to 'bargain.' And these people go from bad to worse, Signore. Terrible things happen. In their inexperience, they become confused in calculating the lira and the dollar, and end up offering me more than I asked in the first place!"

I couldn't help joining the uncle and nephew in a smile at the expense of those unfortunates. Then it occurred to me that I might try out the "system" again. "Down the street," I said, "in the shop on the corner, I saw a nineteenth-century English plate that I would pay fairly for, but there's only a boy there, and he says he doesn't know the price. He wants me to speak to the Signora later, but I shan't be in the neighborhood by the time she returns. How can I . . . ?"

The uncle was on his feet before I had time to finish. "The shop on the corner!" he cried. "The shop of my cousin! I will see what can be done, Signore!" And he was out the door and gone.

My surprise at the speed of the uncle's departure must have shown, for his nephew patted me reassuringly on the shoulder as he handed me my package, now finally done up. "Yes, yes," he said. "The shop of his cousin. A most esteemable woman. Very honest. Do not worry, sir. Wait, sir. Wait."

I didn't have to wait very long. The uncle returned, bearing something folded in newspaper. He unfolded it, beaming. "This is it, Signore? This is the plate?"

It was.

"I have news for you, then, Signore. No sooner had you left the shop than my cousin telephoned. The *ragazzo* told her of your visit, and she told him the price. So now we know the price. Twelve thousand lire, Signore." He quickly raised his hand against my instantaneous look of outrage. "*Calma, calma, signore!* Allow me to finish. Twelve thousand lire, but since you know the Neapolitan system, you know that that means six. And the thousand lire which I know my cousin would offer to me as commission I offer to you. So it is five thousand lire, Signore. Only five thousand lire for this beautiful plate."

"Which is worth one or two at the most," I said. "I might

be willing to pay three, because it happens to match a plate that I already have. But five is crazy, and you know it."

The uncle raised his two hands, his eyebrows, and his shoulders, all at once. "I know, Signore, I know. But it is my cousin's plate, not mine. Were it mine, I would offer it to you gratis, as *omaggio*. But my cousin . . ."

The nephew, who had once again been listening with intense interest, now broke into a torrent of Neapolitan, of which I understood scarcely a word. He was, I could tell, suggesting something to his uncle; the uncle was considering. The nephew finished, and the uncle turned to me.

"Signore," he said, "my cousin is an honorable Neapolitan lady. I think that for this particular plate she was sincerely mistaken in setting her price. I am going to advise her that she reconsider. I am going to advise that instead of twelve thousand lire she ask six thousand, Signore. Would that definitely be acceptable to you?"

The nephew looked at me anxiously. "Do you catch on, sir?" he asked. "Do you catch on? She *asks* six."

I took three thousand lire from my billfold. The nephew burst into another spate of Neapolitan, and the uncle nodded, spoke briefly, and handed him the plate for wrapping. "Since we know that you are in a hurry, sir," the nephew said, "my uncle says he won't ask you to wait until he has actually consulted his cousin. We will take her agreement — how do you say? — for granted."

The lightning two-part drop from twelve to three had left me a bit dizzy, and I heard myself utter an indiscretion. "Suppose," I said, "your cousin *doesn't* agree?"

Both uncle and nephew looked at me with surprise. "But it's the system, Signore!" the uncle said, reproachfully. "The system! We practice it faithfully. I see that even you have not yet grasped the *principle* involved!"

(1965)

62

In the Lobby

Since the building they were living in was turning cooperative and they did not want to buy, Mr. and Mrs. Barnes had
to move, and for months they hunted for a new apartment,
visiting everything they heard of that sounded at all suitable
to their pocketbook and their quiet, rather old-fashioned
tastes. They looked at conventional apartment houses and
remodeled brownstones in half a dozen sections of the city.
To no avail. Then, one evening, Mr. Barnes brought home
a prospectus. "Of course, it's the sort of place we've always
said we'd never live in," he said, apologetically, "but the
location's nice — uptown near the river."

Mrs. Barnes looked at the picture on the folder and made
a face. It showed a great white skyscraper, festooned with
balconies. "It looks like an open refrigerator with the ice
trays pulled halfway out," she said.

"The walls are said to be a little more soundproof than

most," said Mr. Barnes. "Apparently that's the way you judge the new places."

The building, the Barneses found when they arrived, was still unfinished, but in the renting office — a furnished suite of ground-floor rooms entered from a labyrinth of corridors crowded with workmen and smelling of wet plaster — they were made welcome and assigned a "representative," a pleasant-seeming young man who told them his name was Hapgood, "but call me Hap, like everybody else does." The building, Hap told them, would contain almost eight hundred apartments — "every conceivable type of layout" — and Mr. and Mrs. Barnes spent some time looking at floor plans before setting out with him into the vast anthill.

The apartment that had seemed most suitable, judging from the plans, was a two-bedroom affair on a high floor, and when they reached it Hap expounded not only on its particular advantages — its spaciousness, its light, and its views over Manhattan and the river — but also the excellences it shared with all the other apartments in the building. "Security!" he said. "There's a double lock on every door. Our armed guards patrol every floor, every hall, day and night. And here," he said, pointing to a small button in the doorjamb that the Barneses might not have noticed, "is the ultimate in peace of mind. When you go away on a trip, just press this. And you'll know, while you're enjoying your holiday, that should anyone gain access to your apartment despite the double lock *and* the patrol, this button will release an alarm downstairs that will bring armed guards up immediately. It's our way of assuring you a carefree vacation."

The Barneses, who had never lived in a building sufficiently modern to boast an incinerator, were startled to learn that incinerators were now beginning to be passé. "Not an incinerator in the building!" Hap told them. "No smell of burning, no back draft of flames or ash in your face when you open the door of the chute. With us, after the trash goes down, it is carried on a conveyor belt to a pulverizer, and then it is removed in our own sanitary dump trucks. So far, we are the only private apartment house in the city that pulverizes its trash."

Hap permitted himself some drollery as he showed them the model furnished apartments, of which the company was obviously proud but concerning which he was sophisticated enough to admit differences of opinion. "The possibilities of dressing up these units are positively — shall we say — uncanny?" he said, with the suggestion of a smile. (They were viewing a particularly gaudy ensemble that seemed to Mrs. Barnes like the collective brainchild of furniture designers and decorators from another planet.) "Just give your decorator his head and — you see the result."

They saw the several roof gardens, on different levels, decorated with statues imported from Italy; they saw, in the basement, the automatic coffee and sandwich dispensers for house staff and maids and the sauna bath for tenants; and then Hap said that since construction activities had obliged the Barneses to enter the building through a side door, he wanted to show them where the main lobby was to be. Retracing the way they had come along the plaster-smelling corridors, walking at times on gangplanks of sagging boards, they made several turns and emerged in a large space whose surface was littered with lumber, paint cans, and miscellaneous jetsam. "Of course, it's far from finished," Hap began, "but I think your imagination won't find it hard to picture how imposing the vaulted ceiling will be. Notice the portion already completed, over there in the corner. There will be several Venetian chandeliers. The floor will be of waxed —"

Mrs. Barnes gave a little scream. "Look!" she cried, pointing toward the corner that Hap had indicated.

Mr. Barnes looked. He saw a rat, a large black one, under a plaster-smeared wheelbarrow, nibbling at something among the debris. As he looked, it scuttled away.

"— waxed black concrete, marked off into squares by insets of —"

"I saw a rat, Frank!"

"Did you, dear? I missed it." Mr. Barnes was an old hand

at playing down rats and mice whenever glimpsed in Mrs. Barnes's company. Sometimes they cooperated by not showing themselves a second time.

Hap (who, Mr. Barnes decided later, had really seen nothing) allowed himself an interpolation — indeed, a contradiction — slightly patronizing in tone. "The site was given a complete deep fumigation before construction even began. The possibility of rodents is very remote, more remote than anywhere else in the city. Now, we plan to have several large Oriental carpets . . ."

But Mrs. Barnes, her husband knew from the expression on her face, was no longer listening to Hap. She was watching the corner.

"Back here," Hap was saying, "at this other end of the lobby, we've arranged to have an exotic garden designed by a famous landscape architect that will be out of this —"

"There!" cried Mrs. Barnes. "Look!"

Under the wheelbarrow, the rat was nibbling again.

"We ask you to picture the rich effect, especially at night, of the light from the chandeliers on the Oriental carpets and the exotic garden —"

"Here it comes!" Mrs. Barnes said. And indeed, as though attracted by the gorgeous prospect that Hap was painting, the animal came bounding over the rubble, straight toward them. The rat was of good size, very black and sleek-looking. Halfway, it stopped.

"Look! It's glaring at us!" cried Mrs. Barnes, and this time her husband was puzzled — puzzled momentarily — because he recognized that her tone was one not of terror but, rather, of triumph, even elation.

"Jump up here!" he said. There was a large, upturned paint can at hand, on which Mrs. Barnes could take refuge. She usually made for a high place at such a moment. Hap picked up a piece of loose plaster and flung it at the rat, which went scurrying, but even before it disappeared Mr. Barnes saw very clearly that this time his wife was not going to give way. She stood exactly where she had been standing, an expression almost of pleasure on her face, and when the rat had vanished she looked inquiringly, even indulgently, at Hap, as though encouraging him to resume his spiel.

Hap gulped. "Is there anything else that I can show you folks?" he asked, rather pitifully.

Mrs. Barnes looked around her. "Which is the way out, please?" she asked. She asked it as kindly as she could, and Hap dejectedly led them away, glancing at Mrs. Barnes solicitously, but hopelessly, from time to time.

A few minutes later, the Barneses were in a taxi headed downtown. Mrs. Barnes had gone out onto the sidewalk first, and it had taken Mr. Barnes a little time to extricate himself from poor Hap and his embarrassment and apologies. "I didn't have the heart," Mr. Barnes told his wife, "to tell him that for once in your life you welcomed the sight of a rat. It did cut things mercifully short, didn't it? Why can't we arrange to have a rat appear the next time, say, an evening at somebody's house begins to drag? Nobody would blame us for leaving, any more than Hap did."

"Armed guards!" said Mrs. Barnes, with a shudder. "Pulverized trash! Deep fumigation! Why, you'd be taking your life in your hands, moving to such a place! That brave little rat! That *brave* little rat!"

(1964)

The Doomed Terrapin

"Gosh, ain't you never heard of a Gila monster?" cried the boy at the gas station, staring at me in astonishment over his grease gun. "One of the few remainin' relics of the prehistoric ages? And you drove right through Arizona? Heck, you musta passed right through Gila on your way East, too. Say, you sure missed somethin'. *I* saw one, all right.

"Sure was weird," he went on, greasing away. "You see, last summer a couple of guys from my fraternity house in Seattle, and me, we drove around the whole damn continent, thirteen thousand miles, hell-bent every minute. We'd just graduated and we were ready for anythin'. When we began hearin' about this here Gila monster, why, we kept lookin' all over Arizona hopin' to see one. Well, one afternoon we stopped in a little town in the middle of the desert to get some water, and you coulda blown us down if we didn't find out the name of the place was Gila! They told us the monsters was around there in the desert thick as coyotes, and sure enough we'd just driven a little ways outa town when somethin' funny-lookin' started to come right out of the desert and run straight across the road! Gosh, we gave a war whoop and stepped on the gas and just managed to hit the damn thing in time. Say, it was the most God-awful-lookin' thing you ever saw. About a yard long, like a nasty-lookin' lizard, black and or'nge, with a big flat squashed-lookin' head. We hadn't quite killed it when we ran over it, and it kept movin' till it was about five feet off the side of the road, makin' rattlin' noises with its tail and spittin' and hissin' at us. Gosh, when it finally did die, we were glad we'd rid the world of such a screwy-lookin' twirp.

"Well, we were quite pepped up over havin' seen it, anyway, and we drove along another twenty-five miles, and were just gettin' toward the outskirts of Phoenix when suddenly we seen somethin' else crawlin' out of the desert and startin' to cross the road! It looked different from the Gila monster, all right, but it was enough like it to get us up on our ends, and we yelled at this thing, too, but instead of runnin' into it, one of the fellows took up the .22 we had with us and shot it dead, right in the road. Gosh, we piled out of the car to stare at it. It looked sorta like a turtle, only a little queer, sorta. We were pretty disappointed — I guess we had monsters on the brain by that time — and we just took it up and threw it off the road into the desert and drove on again.

"Well, after a few miles, on the outskirts of Phoenix, we found a crowd of people waitin' alongside the road. We always stopped when we seen anythin' interestin', so we stopped and asked what was goin' on and discovered it was a terrapin race. You see, it seems a group of men in Phoenix owned some prize terrapins, and they'd laid a trail of meat or worms or cracker crumbs or somethin' and they'd started all the terrapins off together and now they were waitin' for 'em to come in. Well, we sorta looked at each other, and one of us asked if all the terrapins was accounted for, and they told us all but two. 'All but two, hey?' we said, and hung around a little, and after a while, sure enough a terrapin came amblin' out of the desert right up to where we were all standin', and everybody cheered. 'Just one more, now!' they all said. So we nodded, and said, 'Just one more, hey?' We waited around a little longer, but after a while we said we guessed we wouldn't wait for that last terrapin, as we were sorta in a hurry to get goin' east. Well, everybody wished us luck — even the guy that owned that last terrapin, and that sure made us feel bad. 'Don't know what's keepin' him so long,' he said. 'He was always a pretty good terrapin; hope nothin's happened to him!' Well, we said we hoped so, too, and boy, did we hot-step it through Phoenix and out the other side!

"Made us feel sorta mean, you know, but heck — nobody's got any business lettin' tame terrapins loose in a country full of Gila monsters. That was a sorta consolation to us. We kep' thinkin' that if *we* hadn't got it, a Gila monster probably would've. Don't *you* think it probably would've?"

(1934)

One Round Trip Only

The car that ran into Mrs. Mathews one afternoon as she was crossing the Place de la Concorde was a very small one, but it was quite large enough to break her leg; she herself, amid the squealing of the French brakes, quite distinctly heard her American bone crack. When the driver, a personable young man, tried, at first politely and then insistently, to help her to her feet, she was forced to repeat several times, in the best French she could muster, her firm intention of remaining where she was, on the pavement, to await the arrival of an ambulance. Her stubbornness made him bitter, and he fluently denounced her carelessness, which, he revealed (partly to her and partly to the many spectators who had quickly gathered), was making him disastrously late for an important business appointment with the father of his fiancée. The crowd was won over to his side at once, but Mrs. Mathews lay still, stoical in her pain and unpopularity. Before too long a time had elapsed, a police ambulance arrived, first aid was administered, depositions were taken, and Mrs. Mathews was driven, at her request, to the American Hospital. There she spent the next ten days, after which she was released, with plaster cast and crutches. Ruinous to her budget, but seemingly inescapable, were a hired car and a driver willing to push a wheelchair; and with these she resumed her sightseeing.

Not having been in Paris since before the war, Mrs. Mathews had not seen the pictures of the Impressionists installed in the small museum of the Jeu de Paume, now called the Museum of Impressionism, and it was to this place that she made her first wheelchair excursion. Pierre, her driver and pusher, an amiable young Parisian who seemed amused by the dual nature of his duties, wheeled her up the ramp leading to the museum from the Tuileries Gardens, pronouncing the effort to be *"excellente gymnastique,"* and took her around the ground-floor rooms, containing the earlier paintings. Then, the tour of those rooms completed, she became aware that they were at the bottom of an immensely long flight of stairs, up which he was clearly about to pull her. She was not at all sure she wished him to do so; she was perhaps excessively accident-conscious, but although Pierre seemed husky enough, it was easy to imagine even a stouter man than he wavering and loosening his grip before reaching the top. She was just about to suggest that they content themselves with what they had already seen when a guard stepped forward and offered to help. "It is too bad," he added, touching his cap, "that Madame cannot make use of the elevator."

"The elevator?" said Mrs. Mathews. "There is one? Then why *can't* I make use of it?"

"Because, Madame, it has been transformed into a coatroom. It is a freight, not a passenger, elevator, and so is used very little. For this reason, since it is just next to the entrance, it seemed practical to utilize the space for this other purpose."

"May I see it?" Mrs. Mathews asked, and the guard led them back through the rooms they had already seen, out into the entrance lobby. There, behind a movable counter bearing the sign *"Vestiaire,"* stood a large lady; behind her, an open door led into what seemed to be a small room, equipped with coat racks. "May I," Mrs. Mathews asked the coatroom lady politely, "be allowed to use the elevator for the purpose of ascending to the floor above?"

The coatroom lady smiled kindly, with a glance that showed her understanding of Mrs. Mathews' need, but shook her head. *"Je regrette, Madame,"* she said. "But it is an elevator no longer. It is a coatroom, as you see, and as such is not used for the transportation of passengers."

"But is it in running order? *Can* it climb to the next floor?"

The coatroom lady seemed surprised by the question. "But of course, Madame. It is inspected regularly. Occasionally, when a particularly large picture, such as a wall panel, has to be transported, the coat racks are temporarily removed and it is set in motion. So far as I know, it has never failed in the performance of its duties." Several guards and doorkeepers, attracted by the conversation between the two women, had gathered around, joining the guard who had offered help, and to them collectively the coatroom lady appealed for corroboration. "Am I not right?" she inquired. "Hasn't it always acquitted itself irreproachably?" They supported her solidly, chorusing *"Mais oui"* or *"Bien sûr,"* and staring with what seemed to be a kind of puzzled resentment at this foreigner who was, for some reason, questioning the worthiness of their elevator.

"But then," Mrs. Mathews persisted, "quite *without* giving anyone the trouble of removing any coat racks, wouldn't it be a simple matter just to wheel me in and take me upstairs?"

The coatroom lady's cheeks flooded with red. "Without removing the coat racks!" she cried. "Madame is suggesting, perhaps, that I am lacking in responsibility toward my customers? Would Madame like to think that objects which *she* had confided to the care of a coatroom attendant were allowed by that attendant to circulate freely, at somebody's whim, in a vertical direction or in any other direction? No, Madame! I assure Madame that, despite the character of its installation, my coatroom is a serious and properly conducted establishment, and that objects deposited here are always found by their owners *at the same level at which they were left.*"

In her indignation, the coatroom lady had been far too burningly concerned with clearing her good name to consult with her colleagues, but now, her torrent ended, she looked significantly around at them; in a silence that was even deeper they returned her glance and gave her their support, and then all of them, and the coatroom lady herself, turned on Mrs. Mathews the full weight of the heaviest stares she had ever received. She was reminded of the unpopularity that had surrounded her as she lay on the pavement in the Place de la Concorde, and, suppressing a laugh that would, she felt, have contained a tinge of hysteria, she quietly asked Pierre to take her outside. There, in the sunshine, she did laugh, but Pierre did not. "I am ashamed, Madame," he said solemnly, "ashamed for my compatriots. *Ça, c'est l'administration. Et cette femme — quel gendarme!*"

That evening, Mrs. Mathews told the story to French friends who were dining with her. They assured her that any request for something special or unusual, even though it sprang from special or unusual circumstances, such as her own at the moment, would be apt to be received in similar style by the lower ranks of civil servants — "*les petits fonctionnaires,*" or, as Pierre had called them, "*l'administration.*" "Note," said one of her guests, "that the guard who so politely offered to help you while it was still a question of your reaching the upper floor in the 'normal' way joined the pack against you when you were indiscreet enough to ask someone to take an iota of special responsibility. There's little chance that you'd be allowed to use that elevator unless you were to present a letter from the President of the Republic or, at the very least, from the director of the national museums of France."

74

"Where is *he* to be found?" Mrs. Mathews asked.

Her friend said the office of the national museums was in the Louvre; and as soon as her dinner guests had left her, it was to the Louvre that she addressed a letter.

Shortly thereafter, Mrs. Mathews, finding herself without plans one Sunday, stopped at the theatre-ticket service of her hotel on her way to lunch in the restaurant and asked for an orchestra seat for that day's matinee of *Clérambard,* a comedy by Marcel Aymé that she had been told was amusing. Checking by telephone, the agency employee reported that the orchestra of the theatre, the Comédie des Champs-Elysées, was up one flight from the street but was served by an elevator, and that an aisle seat was available in the first row. Mrs. Mathews bought it. After lunch, Pierre drove her to the theatre and wheeled her into the elevator and from it to her seat, but there the usher, the elevator operator, and an official of the theatre, all of whom had accompanied her and Pierre to assure her well-being, decided that she would be better off in the aisle itself, sitting in her own chair. Wedges were produced from somewhere and placed before and behind the wheels to keep them from rolling; from that position, she very comfortably saw the play.

After the final curtain, Pierre appeared, from the seat that she had told him to buy for himself, to fetch her as arranged, and with him came the theatre official who had escorted her, now full of apologies. The elevator, he regretted to have to say, was no longer running. In some curious Parisian way, which Mrs. Mathews did not quite succeed in understanding, it received its current from another theatre, next door; the matinée in *that* theatre had ended earlier, and everyone had gone home and the current had been turned off. It was entirely his fault, the official said; he had forgotten to tell them next door of Madame's presence; he blamed himself severely. However, a solution existed. If Madame would not mind going backstage, the lift used for transporting scenery was at her disposal. Would she give herself the trouble? She would, and, following their guide,

Pierre pushed the chair down a corridor and through a doorway, pulled it up a few steps and through another doorway, and they found themselves on the stage.

Stagehands were busily completing the destruction of the last scene and beginning the reconstruction of the first. Pierre pushed Mrs. Mathews past the skeleton of a caravan, past the façade of a château. The official, who had hurried ahead to call the elevator, announced that there would be a slight delay; the elevator was at the basement level, being loaded with the four heavy knitting machines that, if Madame would recall, were on the stage at the beginning of Act I. Just then the actor who had played the role of Count Clérambard emerged from his dressing room in street costume. Seeing Mrs. Mathews, he first stared, then doffed his hat and smiled and quickly approached. *"Mes hommages, Madame,"* he said, "and thank you. My colleagues and I noticed you — how could we not notice *une dame si distinguée* — and we deeply appreciated the compliment of your presence." Before Mrs. Mathews could do more than murmur a few suitable words, he said, "You must meet the Countess," briefly disappeared, and returned with his stage wife, in half makeup and a dressing gown and apologizing for her appearance. The actor then produced, from their dressing rooms, the other principals, the viscount and the prostitute, also in incomplete costume. All made complimentary speeches, ending with a general *"Merci, et meilleure santé, Madame,"* and withdrew. By this time, the knitting machines had come up and been unloaded and placed on the stage. The theatre official, with further apologies, saw Pierre and Mrs. Mathews into the elevator, belittled any need for thanking him, and bade them farewell. The operator, when they came to the street level, had a hard time bringing his big car to a landing even with the floor, and when he had finally succeeded in doing so, and had opened the door, he grinned at them and patted the side of the car, as a groom might affectionately pat the neck of a beloved horse. "It isn't often that it carries human passengers, especially a lady," he said. "You must excuse it if its behavior is a little gauche."

Pierre, radiant from his backstage meetings, allowed himself, when he had installed Mrs. Mathews in the car, a respectful general comment in the form of a question: "Does Madame perhaps share the preference for theatres, rather than museums, which I very definitely possess?"

The reply from the director of the national museums of France was, when it finally came, in about two weeks, generally satisfactory; not cordial, perhaps, but decent.

MADAME:

In reply to your valued favor of the second, allow me to confirm that the freight elevator in the Museum of Impressionism has indeed been transformed into a coatroom and is not available for the transportation of passengers. In view of the special circumstances, however, I enclose herewith my permission for you to make use of this elevator *for one round trip only*.

The last words were underlined, as they were also on the typewritten, stamped pass that was enclosed.

Once more, Mrs. Mathews was wheeled up the ramp from the Tuileries Gardens and into the Museum of Impressionism. The coatroom lady affected not to recognize her until she produced the pass, but then it was as though the Museum of Impressionism were suddenly transformed into the Comédie des Champs-Elysées. "*Mais, entrez donc, Madame!*" the lady cried, pushing aside her counter with a powerful gesture, so that the chair could approach the lift. "Come, arrange the coat racks and take Madame up," she called to one of the attendants. "Madame has brought a letter from *Monsieur le directeur*." To Mrs. Mathews she said, "Madame's condition is not a painful one, I hope?" In a moment, the coat racks in the elevator were pushed to one side (there was no mention of the fantasy of removing them), the chair was in, and the car was in motion; a quickly gathered assemblage of guards and attendants were smiling and bowing and touching their caps as it disappeared upward from their view.

Upstairs, reflections on the differences between public and private administration flitted through Mrs. Mathews' mind even while she was savoring the late Renoirs and Monets, the Cézannes, Seurats, Gauguins, and van Goghs, and yet the more she thought, the more she wondered whether her two experiences did show any real difference. In each case, good credentials — a ticket for an orchestra seat, a letter from the director — had brought good will. And if the "gendarme" in the coatroom had been offensive the first time, wasn't her offensiveness balanced by the kindness of the guard who had spontaneously, in the absence of any credentials, offered to help Pierre pull the chair up the stairs? If you looked at it that way hard enough, public and private came out even.

Downstairs again, however, the "one round trip" completed, it did not take long for that carefully balanced viewpoint to topple — in just which direction Mrs. Mathews, despite subsequent pondering, was never quite able to determine. As she emerged with Pierre from the elevator, the coatroom lady was her new, friendly self and expressed the warm hope that they had enjoyed their visit, but when Mrs. Mathews handed her, with thanks, the offering of a hundred francs, which she thought the occasion warranted, the lady passed, in a rush of gratitude, from the merely friendly to the conspiratorial. Quickly snatching something from the drawer of her counter, she thrust it into Mrs. Mathews' hand. "Take it," she whispered fiercely. "Keep it. It says 'one round trip only,' but the next time you present it, who will know that it was ever presented before? Red tape! It is the curse of France, Madame. It relieves one, sometimes, to do a little sabotage — does Madame not agree?"

(1951)

Ciao Fabrizio

The fishing village called — let us say — Matrani is on the Italian coast near Amalfi. I recently visited a friend who lives there, and found it a quiet place most of the week, because that was off season. Weekends it was lively. Families from Naples, who owned villas on the nearby slopes, poured into the village with their guests and their cars, creating an air of carnival — the air, my friend told me, that characterized the place during the months of July and August. During those months, not only did the Neapolitans occupy their villas continuously, but vacationers, both Italian and foreign, crowded the hotels and beaches, and Matrani briefly became a second Capri.

As it was, during the several weeks of my visit the dining terrace of Matrani's best restaurant, La Torre dei Saraceni, was an amusing spot on Friday and Saturday nights. Tables were reserved, and at about nine o'clock the Neapolitans began to arrive — a handsome, decorative set. The ladies, elaborately hairdressed and bejeweled, wore evening gowns that were usually very bright and cut low, and they carried all kinds of scarves and stoles, from chiffon to mink, against the Mediterranean night breeze. The men favored sport shirts, foulards, and cashmere sweaters, above immaculate pastel-colored slacks. Everybody seemed to know everybody. Tables were often placed end to end in advance and decorated with garlands of rambler roses and bougainvillea to await the arrival of a large party coming from a "cocktail" in one or another of the villas; or two or more tables would be pushed together impromptu as groups, arriving separately, coalesced with shrill cries of surprise. I seldom heard an introduction performed. Once in a while, an Ingegnere So-and-So and his wife — who usually seemed to come from Milan — would be presented by their hostess to her fellow Marchese and Contesse and to the assorted gentlemen, but in general the people who came to the terrace were like an enormous lot of cousins transplanted in a body from adjoining Neapolitan town houses to similarly adjacent villas on a single enclosed estate.

One Friday night at the Torre dei Saraceni, my friend and I found ourselves seated close to a particularly long row of tables set for at least twenty persons and strewn not with the usual garden flowers but with dozens of long-stemmed roses, all of the same beautiful variety often seen around Naples — creamy yellow petals edged with crimson. "*Uno sposalizio napoletano*" — a Neapolitan wedding — our waiter told us, and we looked forward to seeing some of the usual weekend habitués gathered together to celebrate this further solidifying of their clan. But when the wedding company arrived, quite late, after all other tables were occupied, they were people we had never seen before except for one, known to my friend as the mayor of Matrani. More formally dressed — the men in dark city suits, and some of the older ladies even wearing hats — they had the same air of high fashion as the rest, and, indeed, during the flurry of seating quite a number of people came over from other tables to shake the hands of the happy pair and of the two older couples who were obviously their parents. The visitors would murmur congratulations — we were struck by a marked softening of their Neapolitan voices, during these moments, as contrasted with the rather strident gaiety they displayed among themselves — and would then return to their own tables. Clearly, the members of this wedding party were *per bene* — known and accepted by the titled crowd from the villas — but also they seemed to be in a curious isolation, self-sufficient and enclosed.

Not that there wasn't some gaiety at the wedding table. The bride's eyes were red, and her mother's eyes, too — one expects a few red eyes at a wedding — but a half-dozen or so adorable small children, who, we guessed, must have been flower girls and pages at the ceremony, kept jumping down from their chairs and moving happily about the table, getting in the way of the waiters and receiving not scoldings but kisses from their elders. And among the guests farthest from the immediate bridal party there was plenty of smiling, gesturing, and calling back and forth.

However, the bride was certainly overwrought. She was a beautiful ash-blonde girl, tall, with a splendid carriage and a classic profile, wearing a low-cut café-au-lait taffeta dress. From time to time, she would dab at her eyes with her handkerchief, and at one point she laid her head on the shoulder of her father, next to whom she sat, and held her handkerchief to her eyes as he caressed her and murmured into her ear. The groom seemed to pay no attention to this. He was a small, mean-looking fellow, lacking even the kind of distinction that his tailor had given his suit, the jacket of which was startlingly wasp-waisted and slashed with exaggerated side vents. The widespread white points of his shirt collar emphasized the pinched, almost scrawny quality of his features and the lumpiness of his Adam's apple. He was young, but there was nothing about him that seemed so; he was like an ageless little clerk. He kept up a grave, unsmiling conversation with his parents — the three of them formed a unit within a unit — and he seemed to have a connection with his beautiful bride only when they stood up together to receive someone's congratulations. At one point, the bride's mother rose abruptly and beckoned to two young women of the party, who were perhaps the bridesmaids. They went to the bride, who rose also, and the four of them left the terrace in a cluster. As they passed us, the bride kept her face averted, but we could hear her sob, and when they returned, after what must have been consolation and repair in the ladies' room, her eyes and her mother's were still red. The bridegroom still seemed unconcerned. Nor did any of the Neapolitans at the other tables react to this evident distress. We wondered whether good manners made them pretend to be unaware, or whether to them everything seemed normal.

Meanwhile, on the harborside promenade just under the restaurant terrace where we were sitting, a crowd had been gathering — a larger crowd than the one on most pleasant weekend nights, when the Matranesi and *paesani* from neighboring villages thronged the pavement along the little fishing port until midnight. There was an air of expectancy, and, indeed, our waiter most exceptionally brought us our bill before we asked for it and urged us not to lose any time. "Signori," he said, "the fireworks will begin very soon now, and you'll want to find a good place. The best view will be from the other side of the harbor, and it will take you a little time to push through the crowd." He pointed to the beach, and, through the darkness, we saw that a sort of framework had been erected and that dim figures were putting finishing touches to what looked like improvised rocket-launching pads. After lingering less long than usual over our coffee, we paid and left. The wedding party was drinking champagne. There were raised glasses and exchanges of greetings, but no speeches or toasts. The ladies were fussing with their handbags; the dinner was ending.

The quay on the far side of the harbor was crowded when we got there, everyone much interested in the half-dozen smartly varnished motor launches that were floating at the foot of the water steps leading down from the mole. Their boatmen, in caps and striped jerseys, were waiting at the wheels, and three or four local fishermen were on duty at the ropes. People in the crowd were telling each other that the craft had been hired in Amalfi — there was nothing to compare with them for rent in poor Matrani. From here, the fireworks installation on the beach could be seen more clearly; the tilted rocket platforms, and the larger contraption that looked like the skeleton for a big roadside billboard.

Then came the wedding party, a procession more or less in irregular double file, advancing along the waterfront from the Torre dei Saraceni. The bride now carried a pale mink stole. The mayor of Matrani was walking ahead of her, motioning importantly to the spectators to make way, and back and forth along the line of march strode the two local carabinieri, occasionally stretching out their arms as symbolic fences. With a series of roars, the motors of the hired launches sprang to life, a fisherman held the first one close to the quay with a boat hook, and after a little flurry over precedence the wedding party began to embark. As each boat filled, it drew away and waited a dozen yards offshore, and when the last boatload took off, all the motors roared in unison, and the entire flotilla took off into the night. The crowd, which had been murmuring in admiration of the fine clothes and lovely women and general elegance of the party, now burst into cheers and shouts: *"Buon viaggio!" "Auguri!" "Addio!" "Ciao!"*

Where was the party off to, in its hired craft? Were they all returning by water to Naples? Would they split up, the bride and groom going perhaps to honeymoon on Capri, only a few miles away? But the bride and groom had not stepped alone into their launch; their two sets of parents had embarked with them. Maybe they were all just going to Amalfi, where the boats had come from, and where hired limousines or their own cars would take them to different destinations. Considering what my friend and I learned later about this wedding party, there must have been plenty of people in the crowd there on the quay who knew its destination and all the facts concerning it. But in Matrani gossip and speculation are infinitely more fun than accurate statement, and all we heard around us was questions and various guesses. Everybody did know one thing: as soon as the boats were far enough off-shore to get the full effect, the fireworks would begin. And scarcely had the last chug of a motor died away when the first illumination burst out. It was the big framework, the set piece, and after some preliminary spluttering and fizzing it revealed itself as truly a great, glowing signboard. In two lines of glittering live letters it proclaimed its message:

CIAO ADRIANA
CIAO FABRIZIO

"*Com'è bello!*" "*Bellissimo!*" "*O!*" "*Guarda!*" the exclamations sprang from the delighted crowd. And then the rockets began. Roman candles, sprays, baskets of flowers — the whole gamut of a fireworks display flung itself into the darkness and out over the Mediterranean. Explosions, rumbles, and swishes vied with human shrieks. The air filled with sulphur, and we saw isolated balls of incandescence swerve from their course and strike the hillsides that half enclosed the port and — for we had been having a drought in Matrani — setting fire to plots of grass and, for all we knew, to houses, or to pieces of the laundry that is perpetually hanging on clotheslines on Matrani terraces.

On and on went the display, and on the upper slopes patches of flame kept appearing, only to be doused by watchful house-holders, who, being true Matranesi, probably did not mind a little charring in return for the fun. Long before the show was over, my friend and I climbed up the steep streets to his house. From his balcony, we saw it end at last in a tremendous aerial bouquet of assorted colors and numerous booms, and, down on the beach — well timed to end with the rest — the gradual fading out of

CIAO ADRIANA
CIAO FABRIZIO

Toward noon the next day, Maria, my friend's cook, arrived as usual with a full market basket, ready to make lunch.

"Well," she said, "this has been an unusual morning. I've done something I don't do every day. I've been to a wedding."

"You have?" my friend said. "We almost went to one last night. At least, we saw the end of one, and you must have, too. How did you like the fireworks?"

Maria stared at us. "You say you saw the end of a wedding last night?" she said slowly. We were all talking Italian, but for a moment she acted as though my friend's words had been uttered in some strange tongue that she had to take time to translate. "What did you see?"

We told her about the *sposalizio* dinner at the Torre dei Saraceni, and the departure of the party. "You must have been watching at least the rest of it from somewhere yourself," my friend said. "Certainly you saw the big illuminated sign wishing luck to the bride and groom?"

Maria shook her head. She began a movement of her right hand that looked suspiciously like the start of a sign of the Cross, then stopped it, probably out of courtesy. "You Americans have the strangest ideas about things," she said, gravely. "No wonder we sometimes ask ourselves whether you are *cristiani*. You obviously understood nothing about what took place last night. Nothing. For one thing, who ever heard of an evening banquet *following* a Christian wedding? The real wedding banquet of those people you saw last night is about to take place now — *now*, at any moment, at the Torre dei Saraceni. And besides —"

"But the waiter told us it was a *sposalizio*," my friend said. "And there was that sign —"

"*Momento*," said Maria. "*Prego*." She held up her hand.

If Maria is a privileged character in my friend's house, it is because she is an extraordinary one. A native of Matrani, untraveled beyond Naples except for one great weekend excursion with a group of pilgrims to St. Peter's in Rome, where she saw the Pope, and only fairly literate, she nonetheless possesses an unusual ability to see events in larger contexts. It was a larger context that she proceeded to sketch for us now, after characteristically asking our permission to do so: "*Permettono, Signori, che racconti una storia?*"

"*Dica*," said my friend.

And Maria began. "A few years ago in Naples," she said, "when they were widening a street, they came on a big underground cemetery" — "*una catacomba*," she called it, "*un ossario piuttosto, molto antico*" — "that nobody knew was there. It was full of skulls and bones, all neatly arranged on shelves cut out of the rock. The engineers were going to clear it out, do away with it, but the people of the neighborhood were furious, and staged a real war. It was *their* cemetery, they said, even if they'd never known anything about it, and they wanted to keep it. They just invaded the place and refused to budge. The women were especially fierce, but plenty of men joined in, and they defended their cemetery like a fortress, and wouldn't let the workmen touch a thing. They won, too. The engineers gave in. They begged to be allowed to straighten the place a little, saying it really wasn't sanitary, but the citizens said we'll do it ourselves, thank you, just leave us alone. So the engineers built a nice entrance and a door — you can see it any time; it looks like one of the entrances to the Naples subway, the Metropolitana, only smaller — and the neighborhood people did do a wonderful job of making the place neat, rearranging bones that had fallen down over the centuries, and sweeping out the corridors.

"And they set up a kind of lottery in the neighborhood, and, according to the number you picked, you could choose your skull. They were most interested in the skulls, of course, they being more human than the rest of the bones. Each person, you might say, *adopted* the skull he or she chose, and sometimes gave it a name, and some people put glass bells over their skulls with labels on them to keep them private and free from dust. The people go down there and talk to them, and say their prayers in front of them. It's a real curiosity, that cemetery — one of the sights of Naples.

"I went to see it once. One of my cousins told me I shouldn't miss it. And the first thing I saw, that morning down there, was a woman of the neighborhood kneeling on a little cushion she'd brought with her, talking to her skull. The glass bell that had been over it was all moist on the inside, and the woman had taken it off and was drying it with her hand-kerchief. 'Poor little thing,' she was saying to the skull, 'how you did sweat during the night! We must think of some way to keep you dry. The night sweat is unhealthy, my darling, but never fear, your Concetta will take care of you. Have faith in your Concetta.' And then she began to say an Ave Maria. Up and down the corridors were other women, and men, too, kneeling on cushions in front of their skulls and murmuring to them. I said to my cousin, 'These skulls are so ancient — aren't they the skulls of *pagani?*' And my cousin said, '*Pagani* or *cristiani*, what's the difference? They're all *morti*, and the *morti* all deserve our prayers and love, because they were once just like us.' "

Maria looked at us. It was clear from her look that she had made a point — one that we should have got, or begun to get. But she is a kindly soul, and, quickly deciding, apparently, that clear though her point was to *her*, we might be forgiven for still remaining in the dark, she went on almost at once. "Nea-politans do more than just respect the dead, Signori," she said. "They love them, and they have many ways of inviting them to go on living with them. That cemetery my cousin took me to is just one example. There was another example in that dinner and fireworks last night, and in the wedding this morning. Did you really think that the name Fabrizio on the fireworks sign was the name of the bridegroom?"

She stopped to enjoy our astonishment.

"Didn't you see how insignificant that little bridegroom was?" she went on. "He's a *barone*, but that doesn't mean much in Naples. Don't you know the story of how one of the old kings of Naples created a hundred or so *baroni* at one sweep, without meaning to? Some tradesmen called on him in a body, at the crack of dawn one morning, with a petition, and they made so much noise in the anteroom that they woke him up. He came out, rubbing his eyes. 'Good morning, *baroni*,' he said sarcastically. 'Thanks for putting me at the top of your list of things to do today.' That was enough for them. They forgot their petition, and every one of them and their descendants called himself *barone* ever after. I think the little *barone* bridegroom must be that kind of a nobleman.

"No, most titles are worth only one thing to a man in Naples — a little money if somebody wants to buy you for his daughter. That's the case in the present instance. The bride's family is very rich. During the war, they left Naples to escape the bombing, and came to Matrani. There were four of them then. The bride was a little girl, of course, and she had a brother a few years older, named Fabrizio. He was killed, here in Matrani, when an army truck ran over him. He was buried in the cemetery here. Later, the rest returned to Naples, but they come every year to visit his grave, and, being Neapolitans, they naturally wanted him to participate in his sister's wedding. So they came to Matrani to celebrate it. They have no villa here, so they hired a lot of hotel rooms for themselves and their guests, and last night they had the prewedding dinner and the fireworks that included Fabrizio. Naturally, the bride was upset, thinking of her brother all the time. She adored him when she was a little girl."

"Where did they go off to in the boats?" my friend asked.

"Only offshore, toward Capri, to look back and see the fireworks," said Maria. "They returned to port after the display was over, and spent the night in their various hotels. By the way, the bride's father is going to have at least one lawsuit on his hands, or anyway a settlement. Donna Teresa, up on the north cliff, wasn't home last night, and when she got back this morning she found a patch of her vineyard burned to cinders by a rocket. Donna Teresa loves her grapes, and she'll expect to be paid for them. But I imagine that rich papa counted on running into some such extra expenses."

That seemed to be the story. But Maria had one more detail to add. "The wedding in the church down below was beautiful this morning," she said. "Lots of flowers, and everybody so dressed up. Naturally, the bride was crying. Especially as they came out of the church. Her father had hired a couple of men to stand outside the church door holding some balloons he'd had made, and as the bride and groom came out the men released the balloons. There were dozens of them, and the wind blew them all over the place, and lots of people grabbed them as souvenirs. Still, a great many of them flew straight up to Heaven, where they were meant to go. Because the bride's father had had something printed on the balloons. A message. Can you guess what it was?"

We got it of course, and Maria nodded. "Yes — 'Ciao Fabrizio,' " she said. "Perhaps they didn't want to take a chance that he hadn't seen the fireworks from so far away."

(1964)

The Griffe
of the Master

The question of whether old Mrs. Ames's picture was really a Géricault or not didn't come up — or at least she hadn't realized that it had come up — until she had owned it for many years: until, in fact, she tried to sell it.

She had bought it as a Géricault, certainly, and with the approval, even on the suggestion, of Alan Dantziger, the expert with the long mustaches, who had guided many of Mrs. Ames's generation of New Yorkers in their viewings of modern art in the days before the Museum of Modern Art had appeared on the scene and disrupted things. "Modern art" in those pre-MOMA days went way back: Mrs. Ames and her friends had been accustomed to call "modern" any art, especially any French art, produced after — well, say after Waterloo. Géricault, Ingres, Delacroix — they were all "modern," until the Museum came along. Or rather, until the Museum developed. To think that one of the first exhibitions of the MOMA, when its premises were still just a few rooms in the Heckscher Building, consisted of a joint show of Corot and Daumier. Mrs. Ames well remembered that winter — how at dinner parties there was invariably talk about those two artists, with people classifying themselves and each other as either "Corotiens" or "Daumiéristes." The first category was "soft," supposedly; the second "hard." Mrs. Ames had boldly '— not entirely sincerely, perhaps — proclaimed herself a "Daumiériste" and had been affectionately laughed at for doing so by her husband (now, eons later, long since gone). Daumier's oils had until then been practically unknown on this side of the Atlantic, and the early Corots, the models and the Italian landscapes, were a revelation to New Yorkers familiar only with the master's nymphs and wispy willows. Corot and Daumier! Who talked about them at New York dinner tables now?

Géricault's style was different — more Romantic, Delacroix-like. There were few of his pictures in New York; only at Alan Dantziger's had Mrs. Ames met up with any, and she had been enthusiastic at once. Alan Dantziger owned two Géricaults, two groups of Arab horses, chestnuts, blacks, and bays, so painted as to be much more than mere horses — rather, "a fascinating vision of forms and colors that had certainly been vouchsafed the painter by the sight of horses, but which remained uncannily independent of them when conveyed in paint: the miracle was the preservation of the vision with the horses nonetheless remaining horses and quite realistic ones at that." That was the way Alan Dantziger was apt to talk about painting to Mrs. Ames and the other ladies whom he shepherded each week during the winter to museums and private collections, including his own, or who would gather with him for an informal little "class," over tea, at one or another of the ladies' homes. "Géricault didn't always sign his pictures, by any means," he went on to say. "But one learns to recognize him. Here, and here, and here, for instance," he said, pointing to an ear, or a fetlock, or a bit of dappling, "are touches that only Géricault would have made

—touches that serve to identify him unmistakably. Details like that reveal what the French call the *griffe* of the master." "The *griffe* of the master" was a phrase much used by Alan Dantziger.

To Mrs. Ames, who told him after the next meeting that she would like to have a Géricault of her own, he said: "I know where there's a small one that may be for sale. An old white horse — a wraith, almost a ghost, but a gleaming ghost, very strange and ethereal. It's in Paris, with my old friend Devaux, in his salesroom in the rue Laffitte. He is *the* Géricault expert. It's a good deal of *his* knowledge that has, if I dare say so, rubbed off onto me." Alan Dantziger stroked his long mustaches in a characteristic gesture of self-deprecation and authority. "At least, the picture I'm speaking of was still with Devaux a few years ago. A little gem. I know he treasures it. You'll be lucky if he lets you have it."

Mrs. Ames paid M. Devaux a thousand dollars for it — no small sum in those Depression days, when one could buy in Paris for two or three hundred dollars a fine little Braque still life that today would bring a hundred times that. "Of course you realize that the price is laughable," M. Devaux told her. "I wouldn't dream of letting it go for that if you weren't a friend of a friend. It's worth double or triple, I assure you."

If that was the case, why was M. Devaux — white-haired, but still spry, and his shop in the rue Laffitte unchanged through war, postwar, and even the swinging sixties — today offering her only the same thousand dollars, after a generation that had been characterized by many things, and not the least striking among them a fantastic boom in the price of pictures, especially French pictures? And — could she be hearing aright? — he was even having the gall to say, "Don't you think it would be nice to give me a friendly ten percent discount, Madame, since we've known each other so long?" Nine hundred dollars, in 1970, for a picture bought for a thousand before the war!

"I really wonder, though . . . Why do you want to sell it, Madame?"

Always an embarrassing question, since the true answer was usually "Because I don't like it." In this case the truth was similarly untellable: "Because I've never really been able to *see* the picture, and now don't see the point of having it around any longer." In fact, the little picture, which in Paris had been a white horse gleaming out of a dark background, with a bit of stable-and-harness still life painted in flecks of blue and red and straw color down in one corner, when hung in New York light had taken on both a glare and an opaqueness that together turned it into a small framed disturbance, a source of annoyance that one wanted off the wall. The little horse had spent most of its American generation in a closet, occasionally brought out and inspected, its quality acknowledged; but always, after a day or an hour of experimental hanging, put back. Here in Paris it looked better at once. "I need the money," Mrs. Ames answered. "I need as much money as I can get."

As she said that, Mrs. Ames could imagine her husband's smile — it was the same smile he gave her when she proclaimed herself a hard-boiled Daumiériste rather than a Corotienne softy — and that her words were instantly recognized as fiction was apparent from an expression of almost impertinent skepticism on the face of M. Devaux. Mrs. Ames reflected that he probably knew to a franc how much her room at the Ritz was costing her; and besides, his conception of the difference between French and American financial circumstances probably did have something genuinely dated about it. He had just been telling her about his sister, who had recently become so *américanisée* as to spend a "colossal fortune" to install central heating in her country house in Normandy, and as a result of that *folie* now found herself "the slave of her furnace" and realized too late that she had "only herself to blame." The disbelief made Mrs. Ames uncomfortable, and not only because it was deserved: it was accompanied by an air of condescension on M. Devaux's part which reminded her of a letter he had sent her soon after she had bought the picture and had written to say that she had forgotten to ask him its history. By "history" she had meant "provenance," but unfortunately, writing in French, she had used the word "*histoire*," and M. Devaux had kindly replied, in English, "I am afraid there is no 'story' attached to the picture, dear Madame. We know nothing of the horse's past life or present circumstances: it is just a picture of a white horse, painted by a master."

Today there was no mention of a master. "The picture has great, great quality, of course, but it is very special," M. Devaux said. And quite without seeming to realize that he was saying something surprising he added: "It is not a picture that I would want to offer for sale. I would keep it for my private collection, and I fear that for purposes of self-indulgence I cannot afford to spend money like my sister."

"But on one occasion you did offer it for sale, M. Devaux. To me."

"No, no, Madame. Forgive me for correcting you. I never *offered* it. *I consented* to sell it — and only because you were a friend of my dear late friend Dantziger. I remember his letter of introduction very well, dear Madame, telling me of your interest and asking me to let the picture go to you, as a favor to him."

That, too, recalled something. In New York Mrs. Ames had invited Alan Dantziger to come to tea and see her new acquisition, and of course she had had to invite Hilde Dantziger as well, Alan's very Teutonic wife, fresh from Germany. Alan often brought Hilde with him when he gave his little talks on "modern art" to the ladies, and her boisterousness kept her from being liked. "Oh, *so hübsch!*" Hilde had cried, at the sight of the white horse. "Ooh! Ooh! *Ganz delikat!* So different from ours! Ours have so much — you know — so much more *oomph!*" And Alan had stroked his mustaches and murmured, "Yes, yes, very lovely. A little — mm — *stranger* than I remembered it, but . . . So you've really bought it, have you? Dear lady, let me raise my teacup to a long and happy association."

At that time Mrs. Ames had barely begun to sense the picture's not too satisfactory self-projection as it hung on her wall, and she realized later that it was the lack of enthusiasm she heard in Alan Dantziger's voice that set off her first twinge of regret about her purchase; for the moment, it was disguised as regret that Alan should be so obviously and easily swayed, in his opinion, by his very assertive wife. Then, later in the conversation, Hilde let fall, in her clumsy way — quite obviously against Alan's intention — the news that Alan had "heard from" M. Devaux just after Mrs. Ames's purchase; and from the pronounced air of awkwardness, even confusion, that engulfed both of them following the disclosure, Mrs. Ames gathered that there had been a commission. That was quite all right, of course, but the secrecy made it less palatable than it might have been.

Today it was M. Devaux whose palatability left something to be desired, and Mrs. Ames rebelled. "Well, you know, M. Devaux, at nine hundred dollars I think I'll just take my picture home again."

"Oh, really, Madame? The poor horse will be bewildered by all these changes of time and atmosphere! He will be quite — do I remember the expression correctly? — off his hay! Come: I'll say twelve hundred dollars, because truly I'll be happy to be reunited with my faithful old Dobbin. That will give you a nice little profit, and . . ."

But Dobbin, withdrawn from a M. Devaux become noticeably cold and formal, accompanied Mrs. Ames back to New York. This was its third Atlantic crossing with her — and in the same cabin trunk; Mrs. Ames still traveled by ship, and this time, on the way, she had plenty of time to wonder what had gone wrong. It was clear that quite apart from his natural stinginess, M. Devaux had been willing only up to a certain amount of money to buy back the horse, but that he had wanted it. His evident coolness on seeing it after an interval had been almost identical with Alan Dantziger's long ago; it gradually dawned on her that neither of them, on re-seeing it, had as much as mentioned the name of Géricault. Alan had not used his beloved phrase "the *griffe* of the master," nor had Devaux uttered any equivalent. For all her own long disappointment in the picture, only now did it occur to her to wonder whether the old Dantziger-Devaux sponsorship of its authorship had crumbled. Had they both decided that it was, after all, not "right," and each for his own reason been unwilling to say so? Had they both, so to speak, backed the wrong horse? Then why had M. Devaux been willing to offer her even a little more than she had paid for it?

Even in the days when "modern" art had included nine-teenth-century art, Mrs. Ames had been no "collector"; her purchases had been few, and when picture prices had begun their dizzy rise, and especially when modern art had become . . . what it had become, her gallery-going grew rarer and she gradually lost what little acquaintance she had with dealers. Now, back in New York, she made a few inquiries, and by different people in the know she was urged to telephone a certain Mr. Baxter. "A knowledgeable and aggressive young Englishman," "well trained and well connected," "sells very effectively from his apartment in the East Seventies" — such were some of the recommendations she had gathered. Mr. Baxter, she was given to understand, was a thoroughly "modern," even "mod," dealer. Perhaps he was what she needed, after old M. Devaux.

She telephoned him, and he came — a young man mod-ishly dressed, at once languid and brisk; in a wild way he recalled Alan Dantziger — the glossy mustaches had been replaced by crimped sideburns, the string tie by a large blue velvet bow. He looked at the picture, examining it carefully front and, more particularly, back. He was anything but silent about its "authenticity." That was the question he raised at once. "I see the picture is unsigned. At least, I find no signature. Of course, if it's there under the varnish or overpainting our rays will locate it. I see no studio mark. No sale stamp. No collector's identification. In other words, all I know about the picture is what you tell me — that Devaux sold it to you as a Géricault. Have you kept his bill, by the way?" And when Mrs. Ames shook her head, Mr. Baxter shook his. "A pity. A totally undocumented picture today, you know, is . . . Alas, today's buyers are not always concerned with quality — as you were, Mrs. Ames. They buy signatures. *Signatures*." He could not deplore that enough, though at the same time making a gesture with descending hands toward the picture that expressed a void, utter nothingness. Mrs. Ames felt a sudden longing, after all, to hear Alan Dantziger pronounce, with his old-fashioned conviction, "The *griffe* of the master" — not necessarily even about her picture, but about some picture, almost any picture, that was "totally undocumented." She knew better than to mention Alan's name — his life's work as spokesman for "modern art" in New York had long since been washed away by the hordes of newer critics and curators; but when Mr. Baxter went on to declare, "Not that anything Devaux might say would be of particular value," she cried, "but . . . he *is* the Géricault expert, isn't he?"

"*Was*, maybe," Mr. Baxter replied. "Experts don't necessarily keep their reputations forever, you know. New knowledge, new methods, dear Mrs. Ames, can make them old hat. In Devaux's case, he must by now be so incredibly ancient and ga-ga . . ."

Ga-ga! Mrs. Ames couldn't believe her ears. And why was it that that word, so confidently uttered by Mr. Baxter, at once suggested its opposite? It flashed on her how very far from ga-ga the old Frenchman probably was; and, more than that, that Baxter had, quite without knowing it, suggested a solution to the mystery of M. Devaux's behavior. Had the old man, perhaps, after deciding that he had been wrong about the picture, perhaps even being aware of his faded reputation as an expert, offered her just what he cautiously thought he could afford, to take it out of the market, to prevent her offering it elsewhere with his old, now reconsidered, attribution? It was only a hunch, but she wondered whether she wasn't right. She felt oddly stimulated by the speculation and had a novel sensation of authority and alertness as she waited for what Mr. Baxter might say next. Following his words about M. Devaux, he had set the white horse upon a table, against a pile of books from the Society Library, sat himself down in front of it, flicking back the long skirt of his green cord jacket, and assumed an air of deep thought. Even with her new wariness, Mrs. Ames was scarcely prepared for the fruit of his meditations.

"This," said Mr. Baxter, "is what I suggest. Facing the fact that complete lack of documentation is a major obstacle, *if* that obstacle could be overcome I'd be able to offer you a nice price for the picture — say $20,000 or so. Now: how to overcome the obstacle? With great luck, a signature or other identification could turn up under X ray. But, let's face it again, that's highly unlikely. Therefore, a major, I might say a *massive*, a *crushing*, authentication is needed. It would have to come from an authority whose name carries simply shattering weight. For a picture like this, the person best equipped to have the examining done, and to write a certificate if he thinks it proper, is good old Augustus." Baxter then added — or, rather, dropped — the surname of a long-celebrated international dealer whose New York establishment was one of the city's few still-existing palaces. "Gusty has a fantastic eye. *Fantastic*. As it happens, I'm on very good terms with him. Used to work with him. It's a spot of his knowledge — if I dare say so — that has rubbed off on me. He regards me more as a protégé than a competitor. So, Mrs. Ames, I suggest: let me take the picture to Augustus. If he finds and certifies that it's a Géricault, then $20,000 or so from me to you. Something around that figure — I might even give you a little more."

There was silence for a moment. Then Mrs. Ames thought her voice very tiny as she inquired: "And if he does not find and certify that it's a Géricault?"

Mr. Baxter did not hesitate. A flourish of enameled cuff

links. "Oh, there's quite a market for minor pictures of this period. People like old horse pictures. There's at least one millionaire who's crackers about them, the way some nuts collect cat pictures. If things didn't turn out, I'd still buy the picture from you. But naturally the price would have to be very different — a fraction."

Mrs. Ames did not ask what fraction. She just stared at Mr. Baxter until she realized that, caught up in her reflections, she was, without meaning to — although there was no question of his not deserving it — staring him out of countenance. One of her reflections was that the degree of naïveté that M. Devaux had attributed to her some thirty-odd years before, when he had thought her capable of asking to be told the "story" of the white horse, and again just a month or two ago, when he had thought she might sell his dear old Dobbin back to him, after a generation of astronomically rising art prices, for less than she had paid — was as nothing compared with what was being attributed to her now by this young New York dealer. Even with her developing cunning Mrs. Ames could not bring herself to *ask* the question that Mr. Baxter's words had generated, but she stared that question at him: "Under the arrangement you propose, what chance do you suggest there might be of this Gusty of yours saying — or, rather, of my being *told* he said — that my picture is a Géricault?" And she wondered, too, thinking of Mr. Baxter's being, in Gusty's eyes, a kind of "protégé," whether some other word might be more appropriate: "assistant," perhaps, or "scout"? Or even "procurer"?

Mrs. Ames's stare had lasted long enough to make Mr. Baxter fidget. He fidgeted a little with his eyes, and there was some fingering of the blue bow tie, but chiefly he fidgeted orally. "I don't know what price you paid for the picture," he said, "but I don't suppose it was very much, considering when you bought it, even if you paid for a Géricault. What I'm getting at is, under the circumstances the $20,000 or whatever you'd receive would be almost entirely profit, and you know about your Treasury Department's twenty-five percent capital gains tax that applies to picture sales. But I wouldn't want you to worry about that. We all agree that it's grossly unfair to penalize a collector who's had the foresight to buy such pictures, and there are ways of reducing the penalty that are perfectly above-board. You'd give me a receipt for whatever sum you'd like me to give you, and you'd deposit my check in the jolly old bank. Deduct from that whatever you paid Devaux for the picture, and give the government boys twenty-five percent of the remainder. Perfectly legal — all you'll have got from me would quite honestly be the check you deposited. And then, next time you go to Europe, there would simply be another check, a banker's draft, or cash if you preferred, waiting for you over there, wherever . . ."

Mrs. Ames scarcely heard the rest. Her ears seemed to close of themselves, and then it seemed easiest to assure Mr. Baxter that she'd think over his proposition, to thank him for his interest, to open the closet door where hung his sealskin coat, and to close the front door behind him as he went out.

She was sure that for the time being, at least, she had no idea what she would do with her white horse — or was it white elephant? But for all that, she couldn't help, especially as she glanced at the picture, still leaning against the books where Mr. Baxter had placed it, having one or two more reflections.

The first was a memory. Wasn't it good old Gusty's famous, immensely respectable firm that had been sued, a few years before, by an almost equally grand rival establishment for having done a bit of wiretapping into its competitor's art transactions?

The second was a vision. Somewhere, perhaps on other paintings and drawings by Géricault, perhaps reproduced in books, she had seen Géricault's rare, much to be desired signature; and now it formed itself quite clearly in her mind — the high and low G, the Romantic flow of the smaller letters, the dashing tall "l" and the looped, slashed "t." On one canvas, with a dark background like hers, hadn't she seen that signature in red? At any rate, that was what she saw now, in her mind's eye — faithful old Dobbin, hanging in a room in Gusty's New York palace, or, more probably, in some similar gallery abroad, perhaps on Bond Street or in Zurich, deposited there after having been acquired from her at the necessarily fractional price, and now bearing, in the lower right-hand corner, just distinguishable amid the harness and the hay, that magic signature, one or two of its red letters half obliterated by "age." How had the name got there? Oh, it was an outrageous fantasy, of course; unimaginable until that moment.

(1970)

Bella Napoli

Because my boat from Capri was late arriving at Naples that spring morning, I missed the connection with the *Principessa di Piemonte*, the tourist steamer for Ischia, and found myself, instead, on a dingy cargo-and-passenger vessel that served not only Ischia but a number of islands at which the *Principessa* did not touch. The majority of the passengers, I gathered from their appearance and conversation, were work-aday folk — island shopkeepers who had been to Naples to replenish their stocks, island farmers who had gone to the mainland to buy animals and agricultural implements, and traveling salesmen. Conspicuous among them by their difference was a prosperous-looking family of Neapolitans — a grandmother, a father and mother, and two boys, about four and six — who, like me, were bound for Ischia on holiday. They made themselves comfortable on one of the wooden benches near where I was sitting in the stern, and the grandmother, a plump, coquettish, dark-haired woman of middle years, seemed to feel called upon to explain their presence aboard this inferior craft.

"My son Carlo, here, is a devil," she loudly informed a young ship's officer who happened to be passing, addressing him casually as she kept flicking a fan that she held in her hand. "All last summer and all through the winter he kept us in the city. We've had no vacation for centuries. We missed the *Principessa* this morning, and if I'd had to wait for the afternoon boat, I'd have simply died of impatience on the dock. I'd rather travel like this than stay in Naples a minute longer." She wore a bright summer dress; golden loops hung from her ears; her bracelets rattled.

"Don't give people the impression that *I* wasn't ready on time," her son retorted. "If you'd have let us get to the dock a few minutes earlier, there'd have been no question of your dying on it. Did you have to start polishing your jewelry while the taxi was standing at the door? Couldn't you have waited? Do you expect shiny jewelry to bring you a new husband, maybe? Maybe even before we get to Ischia?"

I was surprised by his words — in Italy, a parent is seldom addressed so mockingly, especially on such a subject — but the young man seemed to be in a cocky mood, high-spirited, perhaps, at leaving on his long-delayed vacation. His bubble was quickly punctured, however. His mother's eyes flashed, she gasped and clasped her hands to her breast in dramatic, indignant displeasure, and the son's wife looked gravely at him and shook her head. Immediately he apologized. "Forgive me, Mama," he said, looking penitent. "What I said was stupid. Forgive me. Will you? Will you?" He took one of her hands in both of his, like a pleading lover, and released it only when she smiled. Then he kissed her on both cheeks, and the family tension was over.

The passengers on the afterdeck seemed to find the little scene interesting, and they clearly considered it quite natural that it should be played openly, in public; they nodded to one another in approval of the son's apology. But his mother's words about the *Principessa* had not been forgotten, and among the peasants and shopkeepers around me I sensed a certain air of class-conscious defensiveness. When one of the boys demanded lemonade, and the grandmother scornfully replied "Lemonade? On *this* boat? Not before Ischia, *angelo mio*," the honor of the ship was quickly championed. "We have a bar, Signora!" called a passenger from a nearby bench — a farmer in his black Sunday best, who held one arm protectively over a wicker cage of chickens on the bench beside him. "A bar and also a restaurant," he added. Other voices joined him: "Downstairs, Signora!" and "Everything you desire!" they cried, and gestures indicated a companionway. A passing seaman obligingly stopped, leaned over, and called down the steps, "Giuseppe! *Servizio!*"

A steward emerged from below, pulling a soiled white coat over a sweat-soaked undershirt. "I was just getting my kitchen in order," he said apologetically. "There are orders?" Amid cries of "Coffee!," "Beer!," "Lemonade!," he disappeared, and shortly returned with a tray of cold drinks. "The coffee," he said, "is making itself." "Bring us some," ordered the grandmother. "*Subito!* We're dying of thirst and exhaustion."

The two boys took the lemonade their father bought for them to the rail and stood sipping it through straws, and it was from there, after a moment, that the older of them called over, his voice loud and clear above the hum of conversation: "Papa! Why are those men wearing chains on their hands?"

There was a sudden hush. Those of the passengers who had already seen what the boys had just caught sight of nodded sagely or nudged one another, grinning; those who had not yet seen craned their necks or stood up to look. Beyond the companionway, toward the bow, there were two benches, set against the two side walls of the wheelhouse. The one on the starboard side was occupied by a group of five men. Three were khaki-uniformed police with revolvers in their belts; of the two others, one was in striped prison garb and the other in civilian sports clothes, and both held their crossed and fettered hands in their laps.

"Come here instantly," the grandmother ordered the boys. "You, too, Carlo. Stop meddling in things that are ugly," she said to their father, who had started to walk toward the prisoners. He turned back obediently.

I heard passengers murmuring to one another, "Santo Stefano." That was, I knew, the name of one of the remoter islands at which the boat would call. And when I heard others around me knowingly say *"Omicidi"* and "One-way trip," I remembered that there is no capital punishment in Italy and that on Santo Stefano there is a penitentiary for prisoners sentenced to life terms.

The two handcuffed men had looked up briefly as the boy called his question, and then turned away again, uninterested. All five on the bench were talking among themselves, and from time to time one or the other of the convicts, uncomfortable because the length of chain between his handcuffs had slipped from his lap and, dangling, was pulling at his wrists, raised his crossed hands in the air and then carefully lowered them again, with the chain, into his lap; or one of the guards, noticing that the chain had fallen, considerately reached over and raised it. Under his dirty prison jacket of brown and white stripes the one convict wore a collarless white shirt, fastened at the neck with a protruding, incongruous gilt button. He was a small man, almost elderly, with a pinched face that bore an expression of meekness and resignation; his extreme pallor told of long confinement — probably on the mainland, because of a lengthy and finally fruitless appeal — before this exile to Santo Stefano. On his head was ignobly perched a kind of white cotton prison beret, which looked like some foolish bit of headgear worn by a circus clown. The other, in contrast, was a brutally handsome, tanned young man with wavy black hair; his slacks were of a smart, light material, his shirt was gaily checked; had it not been for his chains, he might have been a holiday passenger on the *Principessa*. He was talking animatedly, his white teeth flashing as he smiled.

The boy's question put an end to the group's isolation. One

by one, with that apparent aimlessness, that utter casualness, of which Italian men are such masters, a number of the male passengers left their seats. They strolled here and there; they stood at the rail, staring out over the blue waters of the gulf and the deeper-blue silhouette of Capri; gradually they approached the bench; and before long they had formed a human hedge around the prisoners.

"Such high-class attractions we have on board!" the grandmother cried. "At least we can no longer see them. From here, we can consider that they do not exist."

After our boat had made its first brief stop, at the island of Procida, I moved away from the stern and went forward. The handcuffed young man in the bright shirt had been recognized, I discovered when I arrived at the outskirts of the group standing around the prisoners. His photograph, a man beside me was telling another, had only recently appeared in the Naples newspapers along with the story of his crime; it was his first — the double murder of his fiancée and his brother, whom he had tracked to their secret meeting place.

Then I began to hear what the two prisoners were saying. "I have important friends," the young one was boasting. "Friends with influence. It was they who got me permission to travel in these clothes. Dressing this way makes all the difference."

"To you, perhaps," the older convict said. "But is anyone else impressed?" As he spoke, his face lost some of its meekness; his parted lips showed sharp little teeth, and his faded blue eyes had a level, penetrating stare.

"Oh, many people!" The young man flashed a bold smile. He looked around at the crowd; he seemed delighted by the interest he was arousing. Traveling from Naples to the islands on their shabby boat, these passengers had doubtless seen many handcuffed murderers, but he was one of the more celebrated; they were enjoying his company. "Many! Many!" he boasted, using the feminine, *molte*. "A good appearance, you know, like mine . . . I could tell you things!"

"Please spare us," the older convict said. "Think of our modesty." Some of the passengers laughed. "Are you really so featherbrained," he asked sarcastically, "wearing those bracelets on your wrists, as to think that the color of your shirt and trousers still counts for anything with anybody? In any case, I assure you that at Santo Stefano — "

The young man interrupted passionately. "Even at Santo Stefano!" he shouted into the other's face. "Even at Santo Stefano, I'll have permission! My friends in Naples promised. Their promise will be confirmed. You'll see — I'll dress like this always. Never like you!"

He looked beseechingly at the guards as though for corroboration. But the guards' skepticism was all too apparent; they were smiling sardonically at each other, their eyebrows raised. The young man saw them, and it was as though suddenly, and only at that moment, he realized his plight. His face contorted, and he gave a choked-sounding cry and raised his chained, crossed hands high into the air. It seemed as if he meant to crash them down on the head of his tormentor. A gasp arose from the crowd and the guards sprang forward. But the young man's gesture was wholly one of despair; he lowered his hands into his lap and a tremor went through his body, and he twisted violently around so that he was staring away from everyone, his face pressed hard against the wall of the wheelhouse.

There was a sudden movement in the human hedge of which I formed a part. Someone was none too gently pushing his way through; it was, I saw, Carlo, the young father, escaped, after all, from his mother's vigilance. No one protested as he jostled and trod on feet without even saying *"Permesso,"* and when he reached the front, he addressed one of the guards abruptly. "I recognized that one right away, from my seat," he said, pointing at the younger convict. "But who's this one? What's his story?"

The guard stared at him a moment, then shrugged.

"A crime of passion also?" the father persisted. "Jealousy? A woman?"

It was the same cockiness, the same lack of manners that he had shown in his unsuitable jest to his mother, and since she was not there to reprove him, he was reproved by everyone present. The utter silence of those who formed the hedge, the closed expressions on the faces of the guards, the steady, unblinking stare of the older convict — dignified despite his stripes and his clown's beret — all told him that his questions had been found offensive. Even the young murderer turned part way around, to see what manner of man it was who would behave so. "A woman?" the father repeated, and this time the guard did not even shrug. The father's face reddened; resentment, embarrassment, longing that someone would speak to him — his expression was eloquent of all those.

Toward the stern, the steward had been calling "Coffee! Coffee is ready! Coffee!" and had emptied his trayful of little cups. Then he had descended to his kitchen, replenished his tray, and come up again. He approached us now in the bow; the aroma of coffee was about us. "Coffee? Coffee, Signori?" he cried.

With a glance at the tray of steaming coffee cups, the older convict ostentatiously sniffed. "How good it smells," he murmured. He seemed to address no one in particular, but as soon as his words were uttered, he fixed on the young father a stare, half smiling and half taunting, that amounted to a dare. Under his steady look, the young father registered discomfort, hesitation, uncertainty, all the stronger since not only the convict was staring at him; the watching faces of those about me told me that they were all waiting to see his move. Already, since our departure from Naples, they had seen him make one apology they considered seemly; now they were awaiting a second, which in their opinion was clearly just as much called for. It was a moment of suspense; the young father had only to signal to the steward, to order coffee for the men on the bench, and he would redeem himself as becomingly and completely as he had with his mother. But he hesitated too long. A call came from the stern, a shrill, indignant feminine call — "Car-lo! Car-lo!" — and his moment of opportunity was gone. No one was unaware whose summons it was, and to no one, least of all to him, did it occur that he might disregard it. Spontaneously, a gap opened up in the hedge, and, carefully looking at no one, he made his passage through it. No one spoke, few glances were exchanged; the gap in the hedge closed behind him.

It was a rustic-looking individual, obviously one of the ship's habitual passengers, who treated the convicts to coffee, and they drank it gratefully, their chains clanking as they clumsily raised and lowered their cups.

Everyone was now staring at Ischia, which the ship was rapidly approaching. A road lined with pink and white houses followed the curve of a harbor; pleasant villas stood in pine groves; hillsides were green with vineyards. The engines reduced their speed and the normal speaking voices of more distant passengers could be heard. "These beautiful islands!" came the voice of the grandmother. "Vacation at last! *Bella Napoli* — the farther I leave it behind me, the more light-hearted I feel!"

Her words made the younger convict look out desperately across the bay, toward where Naples had disappeared on the horizon. The older man laughed harshly. "What's the matter?" he gibed. "Afraid you'll never be back? You will be, though, barring accident. Whenever there's time, they ship you to a Naples hospital for the end. 'See Naples and die,' you know. They respect the old saying on Santo Stefano."

(1952)

A Ride with Ralph

At Raton, late one afternoon, we transcontinental passengers were waiting in our places, wondering whether we would approve of the new driver who was to take us on to Santa Fe and Albuquerque, when we suddenly heard the group of drivers lounging outside the bus station burst into a cheer. "Yeah, Ralph!" they cried, and we saw a blond and very boyish giant coming toward us, wearing the company's uniform and a dazzling pair of new cowhide boots. "So long, boys!" he called, looking very handsome and serious, and after climbing on board and examining our tickets, he at once made himself as popular within the bus as he seemed to be without.

"Well, folks," he said earnestly, facing us all, "I'll be with you as far as Albuquerque, and I hope you'll like me as much as I know I'll like you all. I'll do my best to be satisfactory, and I'll do everything in my power to give you a fine ride. It's mighty dandy country through these parts, and I hope you enjoy it. If you have any suggestions or complaints, I'll be glad to have 'em. Let's go!" He swung into his seat, there was an appreciative murmur, and we were off.

Since I rode just beside Ralph in the front seat, we soon fell to talking, and long before we made our first comfort stop — the bus halts considerately every two hours from New York to Los Angeles — he had revealed that a certain subject was very much on his mind. "A pair of boots is quite an investment," he stated. "Have you any idea of what a good pair of boots costs?" I confessed ignorance. "If I was to buy them retail, in a regular swell shoestore in Denver," he informed me, "they'd cost me plenty, and I'd go without. But anybody's foolish to go to those swell stores; what you do is to write to a firm in K.C., give 'em your measurements, and you get a fine pair of boots by mail. It's a sort of wholesale proposition, see, and it certainly is worthwhile. But would you believe it, even buyin' 'em that way, these boots set me back sixteen bucks; you can see they're quite an investment."

I pointed out that so handsome a pair was worth investing in, but admitted that I was disappointed to hear that they weren't real New Mexican boots, and that they came from Kansas City. "You can buy two kinds of boots in New Mexico," Ralph told me. "You can buy common ordinary boots that ain't worth half what you pay for 'em, and you can buy the best boots in the world — made of imported kangaroo hide — but you've got to be richer than you and me to get *them*. They'll set you back anywhere from fifty to a hundred bucks. But oh, man, they're soft as velvet and sure worth it if you got the dough. Now, these boots are OK, but you know they're — they're — uh, beginnin' to pinch a little. As a matter of fact, they're — they're beginnin' to hurt me quite a good deal. Isn't that funny?"

I said I thought it was anything but funny, and Ralph agreed. "It ain't funny a heck of a bit," he revealed. "They sure feel pretty bad, and I've got to do something about it pretty quick. I've got a friend up here in Wagon Mound; he'll fix me up. We stop there ten minutes anyway."

"Well, you'd better get to Wagon Mound as fast as you can," I suggested. "You don't want to be in misery."

"That's right," said Ralph. "I don't know whether it's the cowhide beginnin' to bind, or my feet beginnin' to swell, but it's gettin' worse every minute." He took my advice with thrilling literalness, and we rushed over the road at a rate that permitted him to talk no more. I watched the speedometer go from the usual fifty to fifty-five, to sixty and a little over. It was dark by now, and after a breathless half hour a cluster of lights appeared and we drew up in front of a ramshackle chili joint. "Folks," said Ralph, switching on the lights and turning around to us, "this is Wagon Mound. It ain't much of a place, but you'll find some good chili inside the café and the comfort stations are around to the left. We'll be here ten minutes." He gave me an intent glance. "I'm in torture," he confided in a low voice, and disappeared.

The passengers followed him, but the chili joint struck me as uninviting, and I remained in the bus. After a while they began to drift back, very garrulous and interested. "The driver's certainly having a hell of a time with those new boots," one of them announced. "He's got a Mexican in there trying to pull them off and they won't budge; whenever the Mexican pulls, the driver yells and says he's taking his skin off, and they don't seem to be getting any place. He's afraid he's gonna have to cut 'em off, and he hates to do that. They're brand-new." As the bus filled, everyone talked of Ralph and his boots; we remained in Wagon Mound a good deal longer than ten minutes, but finally Ralph limped in, still wearing his cowhides, and in a bad mood. He made no reply to our sympathetic inquiries, informed us crossly that the next stop would be Las Vegas, switched off the lights, and drove on. "The next stop'll be Las Vegas if I live to get the hell there," I heard him mutter mirthlessly in the darkness, but as I was not sure whether he was addressing me or not, I judged it wiser not to reply.

The ride to Las Vegas, accomplished in considerably less than the scheduled time, made the spurt to Wagon Mound seem stodgy, and after telling us that we had something over half an hour for our supper, Ralph limped away out of sight. Speculation was vociferous as we ate at a long counter, and bets were made as to whether he would reappear with or without his boots. Nobody got into the bus, but all waited near it, to get a good view, and the silence of pity fell over us when Ralph emerged limping, still booted, from the gloom of some nearby buildings. "All aboard," he called, in a voice in which despair had taken the place of surliness. "All aboard, folks. We make no stop between here and Santa Fe." We filed somberly aboard. I was the last, and could not resist murmuring that it was too bad. "Get in, buddy," said the boy, dully. "If I go nuts, you grab the wheel."

For the sake of all of us, I hoped Ralph wouldn't go nuts, for evidently Santa Fe contained further possibility of aid, and we tore through the darkness like a shell, Ralph's hands now and again straying alarmingly and futilely from the wheel to his boots. After a long stretch of silence he looked around, evidently to see if I was there, and after clearing his throat a few times he asked, in a private, piteous, small voice, "*You* don't happen to know anything about pullin' off boots, do you, buddy?" I replied just as privately that while I had never done it, I should be glad to try, but at this he merely shook his head, and drove on. Unspoken sympathy filled the speeding bus. Ralph's misery seemed to permeate us all; the ride began to seem endless. Then, suddenly, all was changed. Dramatically, far ahead in the darkness on the road we saw a waving light; Ralph shoved on his brakes, which hissed alarmingly, and as we all stared he opened the door to a Mexican, who blew out his lantern, climbed in, and asked for a ticket to Santa Fe. This transaction took a little time, and though I couldn't understand the Spanish, I realized that Ralph and the Mexican were conversing about something other than the ticket. Finally, after the Mexican had uttered several emphatic statements, Ralph abruptly killed the motor and turned to us. "Folks," he announced, "I can't go on like this! If you'll have the kindness to put up with a few minutes' delay, I'll sure appreciate it. This friend of mine is going to perform some first aid, and then we'll shoot right along. Is that OK with everybody?" We all called out our assent, and preparations began. Ralph left the wheel, sat on the step of the bus, and stretched out one leg; the Mexican turned his back, straddled Ralph's leg, grasped the enormous boot tightly, found a footing, and bent forward; Ralph, holding onto the bus, placed his other foot firmly against the Mexican's posterior, and while one pulled, the other pushed, and both grunted. Everyone crowded to watch. The Mexican manipulated the toe and heel, and Ralph shoved with all the strength of his gigantic self. It appeared hopeless at first; the leather was so tight about Ralph's great calf and foot that it seemed to be almost part of him. That was evidently the way it felt to him, too; he whispered and cursed. Finally, the boot began wonderfully to move, and after a few particularly Herculean efforts, it actually slipped forward and the Mexican fell flat on his face, the boot clutched triumphantly in his hands. The crowd exclaimed with delight; Ralph whispered to himself some more, and stretched out his other leg, the Mexican manipulated as deftly as before, and was rewarded by falling flat on his face once again.

We were all much impressed by the way Ralph sat with his head in his hands for a few moments. "Does that relieve you?" I asked him, when he finally breathed deeply and looked around at us.

"Relieve me!" he cried. "Take it from me, folks, there's one boy that knows what heaven is now!"

Obviously, Ralph couldn't drive us to Santa Fe with only stockings on his feet, so I offered him my slippers, which were in the suitcase on the rack above me; he gingerly slipped his sore toes into them, and after a little experimenting decided he could make them do by wearing them as mules. "All right, folks!" he called, when he had thanked us. "Everything's OK now. Let's go to Santa Fe!" Cheers arose, he switched out the lights, and we were off. The Mexican hero grinned himself into a snoring sleep, and for the next hour and a half we tore over the mountains, making up for lost time.

"This is Santa Fe, folks; we'll be here ten minutes!" Ralph called out when we had rolled through the dark streets to the station. "The comfort stations are at the rear of the waiting-room!" I was going to stop over in Santa Fe for the night, so when the passengers dismounted, Ralph handed me my suitcase and bade me farewell, standing beside the bus in my slippers. "It's sure nice of you to let me wear these to Albuquerque," he said earnestly. "I just don't know what I'd do without 'em. Because those boots" — he almost smiled — "those boots, well, I sure couldn't wear *them* to Albuquerque!"

"No," I said. "You'd better send them back to K.C., don't you think?"

He ignored this. "The slippers will be waitin' for you here when you take your bus tomorrow night," he replied. "I sure hope you have a good trip all the way to L.A., and I'm sorry I won't be drivin' you."

I was sorry, too. The drivers between Santa Fe and L.A. were all good fellows, but none of them was quite the boy Ralph was, and his absence was hardly compensated for even by the note which I had found with my slippers in the bus station the next night. "Dear Friend," it said, "I am deeply grateful to you for letting me use your slippers. They came in very handy. On inspection I note they are in rather poor condition and as I know my feet are large if I am responsible for the damage I would be glad to have them sewed if you would leave them together with your address. Yours truly, Ralph L."

(1934)

115

The Fair Singer

Breakfast, Mrs. Ives told me, would be at eight — or would I prefer quarter to? I said that eight would be splendid, and I added, perhaps a little familiarly for a newcomer, "The later the better, as far as I'm concerned." I saw a glance pass between the Ebbets, Mrs. Ives's couple. Had my answer been chalked up as bad? Had I got off to a poor start within half an hour of my arrival?

From the moment I had first known, back in New York, that I was going West, I had been reminding myself to show Mr. and Mrs. Ebbet particular consideration. They were new in Mrs. Ives's service, and they weren't real domestics. "In Indiana, before he lost his position in the crash, Mr. Ebbet was a bank clerk, but he drives my car beautifully and serves very nicely," Mrs. Ives had written me, describing her California household. "Mrs. Ebbet is a first-class cook. She used to bake for church suppers all over her rural area." It was a delicate situation. The Ebbets had probably already guessed that financially I was in a boat similar to their own. The difference — and it could only gall them — was that I was a guest, a friend of Mrs. Ives's nephew.

Bob Ives and I had been in the same department until the college, Depression-struck, rid itself of several young unmarried instructors, me among them, at the end of the first semester. I had spoken to him about wanting a quiet month or two in new surroundings to get started on work of my own, and it had been his idea that his aunt should invite me to California. She was an elderly Seattle lady, he told me, childless, lonely since her husband's death, who would probably be glad of young company in her winter house near Santa Barbara. He put us in touch by correspondence, and here I was, groggy from a bus trip across the continent.

As to the Ebbets, it was grim enough for middle-class people down on their luck to become servants to someone well off: to have to serve that person's hanger-on might be thoroughly repugnant. I had told myself that again and again. Now I did so once more, as we all said good-night and went to bed. It was early, barely ten o'clock; but quite apart from the urging of my bus-punished bones (in the thirties many of the main highways west of the Mississippi weren't hard-top) it was evident that this was no house for late hours.

It seemed only a few minutes later when from deepest sleep I was awakened by what I gradually realized was a knocking on my door. Opening my eyes I saw that the room was full of gray light, and there was brightness around the edges of the window shades. Eight o'clock already? "Yes!" I called. "Five minutes!"

"May I come in?" called a voice — Mrs. Ives's.

Hastily pulling back the bedclothes I had just thrown down, I cried "Come!" The door opened, and my hostess stood there clasping a mauve kimono about her. My vision was blurred, but even so I was struck again, as I had been the night before, by how daintily tiny, how pretty, Mrs.

Ives was. She had very fine, very white hair, of a luxuriance and whiteness that spoke of health and care, and even at this hour it was in perfect order, piled rather high; her eyes were a wide-awake blue, and her cheeks, though wrinkled, were pink; her small nose and mouth were those of a girl. One could see that as a young woman she must have been immensely attractive. "If you'll get up quickly and come into my room," she said, "I think you'll forgive me for waking you." She withdrew, and as I blearily fumbled for bathrobe and slippers I saw that my clock showed quarter to six.

"Choose your window," Mrs. Ives said, when I entered her room. "But don't stay too long at it, or you'll lose the best of the rest."

There was no denying the glory of that mountain sunrise. The horizon toward which I looked from the first window was a series of jagged, nearly naked peaks; here and there among them snowfields blazed orange-red, and the crags, glowing and tawny at their tops, shaded down quickly into gray and purple. Beyond the other windows there was a Greek-theatre arc of high white snow, against the melting ice-cream cloud-colors of the eastern sky. Mrs. Ives's room, I gradually became aware, with windows on three sides, was close to the prow of a spurlike hill on which her house was built; all around, just below, clung narrow terrace-gardens like the decks of a ship; several hundred feet farther down lay a curving, fertile-looking green valley, a mile or so across, rimmed by foothills that rose into the high mountains.

We both watched silently for a few minutes, and then Mrs. Ives pointed to a cleft in the range to the west. That was the pass, she said, over which we had driven in the dark the night before, after she and the Ebbets had picked me up at the Santa Barbara bus station. "And speaking of the Ebbets," she continued, not entirely smoothly, "there is a member of the household you haven't met yet."

Mrs. Ives's delivery of those last words contained such a hint of what seemed to be coyness, that as I listened for their sequel I was expecting to learn that the Ebbets had with them a tiresomely beloved pet — a poodle, perhaps, or some venerable tabby they hadn't been able to bring themselves to part with and to which homage would have to be paid. "Yes, Mr. Ebbet's eighteen-year-old niece," said Mrs. Ives. "She's their ward, as well — an orphan. There was nothing for her in that country town, and she's staying with them here until other arrangements can be made."

There was a brief pause. "Other arrangements?" I said. Mrs. Ives seemed to expect me to say something.

Mrs. Ives nodded. "Something she can do. I don't know what they have in mind. There was an emergency of some kind in Indiana. It all happened suddenly, and very recently. There wasn't time for me to write you or Bob about it before you left New York. The girl has been here only a week. I wanted to write, to warn you, because . . ."

Perhaps I might have been brighter at a different hour, but I quite misunderstood what Mrs. Ives was driving at. What I thought she was doing was apologizing to me for my not being, after all, her only guest, as she had indicated I would be. She was afraid that the presence of someone else in the house would be a disturbance, would distract me from the work I hoped to do. "Please, it's perfectly all right," I assured her. "I'm pretty adaptable. Don't think that . . ."

Mrs. Ives hesitated a moment and then seemed to take a plunge: of course the poor lady had counted on my quicker comprehension. "You see," she interrupted me, "I hadn't yet told the Ebbets about your coming when they learned of the niece's emergency. I was just about to tell them. So when they brought me the news, and asked whether she could use the empty servant's room, live here — and I felt I had to say she could — it was awkward having at that same moment to announce *your* coming. Of course I don't mean that *I* feel the situation is awkward. *I* have no uneasiness on that score. I know that you are a gentleman."

I squirmed: being called a gentleman is so often like being told by one's British acquaintances that one doesn't seem at all American.

"It's Mrs. Ebbet. My feeling of awkwardness came from sensing what Mrs. Ebbet was thinking. She was certainly much taken aback when I broke the news about you. I think she almost regretted having suggested the niece. I reassured her. I told you you were a friend of my nephew's and that everything would be perfectly all right, and she said — she *said* — that I mustn't think she had any worries about it, they were enormously grateful, and so on. So I *think* she's decided to be all right about it. But they're very respectable people, and — well, a girl of eighteen in the house with a young man — I felt that as soon as you came I should . . ."

"Thank you for telling me," I said. "I'll watch out, I promise you. Please assure the Ebbets . . ."

At that point an utterly unsuppressable yawn cut into my words. Mrs. Ives stood up immediately. "Go back to bed, you poor man," she said. "And we shan't expect you for any eight o'clock breakfast. Just sleep as long as you like."

The yawn had been no indication of boredom — indeed I was aware that a situation of some piquancy might be developing around me; but the hour was, after all . . . sunrise. However, the alacrity with which Mrs. Ives responded to the yawn made me suspect the role of the color-symphony that was now beginning to subside outside the windows. Had it been principally an excuse, an occasion for a talk in private? Mrs. Ives sounded so relieved, with her warning out of the way.

"Since you're here," she said, as I moved toward the hall, "let me show you something that I hope you will feel free to use." She opened a door and switched on a light: "This is the scales closet." Almost automatically I stepped onto the platform scale that stood there, and fingered the weights. On the white wall were neatly penciled two notations: "2 lb. 12 oz." and "1 lb. 2 oz." "My husband weighed himself on those scales every morning after his bath," Mrs. Ives said. "See how he reminded himself of the weights of his two dressing gowns, the wool and the silk. He never could remember them. He subtracted one or the other from whatever total weight the scale said."

"Subtracted them? Oh yes, I see."

After a moment of reflection I distractedly murmured, "Good-night," which made Mrs. Ives laugh, and I made my way down the hall and back into bed.

When I awoke several hours later, I heard singing. I couldn't tell whether it came from a gramophone or a radio, nor could I identify the song — something soprano and showy.

I shaved and showered, and as I opened the door from the bedroom wing a different song burst upon me. This one I knew well, but I was surprised to hear its voluptuousness being rendered not only live in the morning, but as a duet. From the hallway I saw, in the living room, a charming scene. Mrs. Ives, and Mrs. Ebbet in a housedress, were sitting side by side on the bench at the grand piano, four hands going strong and both ladies intent on their score; and bending over them were the singers — Mr. Ebbet, who held a feather duster in one hand, and a blond girl wearing an apron. Both were reading with as much concentration as the accompanists. Their voices — a lovely soprano that plunged deep and soared high, and a true tenor — poured out richly and easily. Their pronunciation was noteworthy in a different way, and at this moment they were sailing into a reprise of the opening words: *Mohn koor soo-ver at-ta voyks* . . .

I stayed outside until they finished, then quickly applauded and showed myself, and there was a round of good-mornings. It was not Mrs. Ives, but Mrs. Ebbet, who introduced me to the girl — "our niece, June." She stared at me with the frankest curiosity, and I probably looked similarly at her, as Mrs. Ebbet continued to talk. "We Ebbets usually make our music after lunch," she told me, closing the score. "Mrs. Ives is kind enough to turn the living room over to us every day while she takes her afternoon nap. But today when we were finishing straightening up she came in and started playing one of the songs we left here yesterday. Before we knew it we were all pitching in. Usually June and I improvise a four-hand arrangement, while she or my husband sings. Or I just accompany. In that song you just heard, Mr. Ebbet improvised his vocal harmony. It's really a woman's song, by the French religious composer Saint Saynes."

I said I'd had no idea that I'd be entering a musical household.

"Nor had we when we came," said Mrs. Ebbet. "We were amazed to find Mrs. Ives such an excellent pianist. Why, her little fingers fly over the keys faster than most people's half her age. We enjoy having her play with us."

Mrs. Ives looked down in the direction of her "little fingers" with an air of modesty that I imagined might veil some lack of gratitude at being welcomed to her own piano. Then she raised her eyes and severely addressed the soprano. "I can't help saying again, June, that with a voice like yours it's folly to smoke at all, let alone chain-smoke, as you call it."

June was not smoking, but she had just taken a pack of cigarettes from a pocket of her dress, and now she put it back again. She gave a little shrug. "I don't think it's very important, Mrs. Ives," she answered, politely. "It's not as though I was going to make a career of singing, or anything like that."

"You have an unusually lovely voice," said Mrs. Ives firmly, "and to such a gift you owe respect."

Mrs. Ives stood up, and the others made their way toward the kitchen, Mr. Ebbet giving a few whisks of his feather duster as he went.

Before lunch Mrs. Ives took me on a tour of her property. It was called "El Espolón" — The Spur — and indeed its top surface was so narrow that even on the principal façade, along the open side of a paved "patio," which was enclosed by the house on the other three sides, there was space for only the slenderest strip of lawn. Beyond that, over a hedge of geraniums, was part of the precipice and the vast view of valley and mountains that I had seen at sunrise. Much of the foothills and most of the mountains on the horizon, Mrs. Ives told me, were a trail-crossed preserve, one of the National Forests. We walked along the precipitous sides of the spur, a comfortable and perfumed stroll on gently sloping, well-kept gravel paths between terraces of oranges and lemons, avocados, almonds, and persimmons.

Some of the persimmons appeared as dessert at lunch, which was served by Mr. Ebbet wearing a gray alpaca jacket and white mesh gloves through which dark hairs bristled. Mrs. Ebbet's dishes were exquisitely plain, the kind Americans so often long for in vain abroad (and at home, too, for that matter): herbless, all but sauceless, with the lightest seasoning, the flavor of the meat and vegetables rendered by perfect cooking, not concocting. The persimmons were opened out on the plates like flowers, with corollas of whipped cream.

As we drank our coffee in the patio Mrs. Ives proposed a drive. She rang, intending to ask Mr. Ebbet to be ready to take us out a little later, but it was Mrs. Ebbet who came, and with a long face. Her husband had suddenly discovered that he had a temperature, she said. Close to a hundred. She murmured something about "last night . . . the night air." He couldn't possibly go out. Would Mrs. Ives like June to drive us, instead? She handled a car well, had a license. I said there was no need for any chauffeur except myself, if no one objected. No one did, and Mrs. Ebbet fetched me the keys to the garage and the Franklin.

"Is 'close to a hundred' enough to look so very worried about?" Mrs. Ives asked me when we were alone. But I had heard Mr. Ebbet coughing in the kitchen during lunch, between his appearances at table, and if there was any question of his having caught cold during the drive to meet me the night before, I was only too glad to help make amends.

Our ride gave me a good idea of the valley, in more ways than one.

Its floor was a paradise of citrus groves, belonging to year-round commercial growers, who lived in wooden or stucco bungalows among their trees. The lower slopes of the hills were dotted with fancier houses — winter houses like El Espolón, most of which had small terraced groves of their own. There was a village, with shops, a post office, and several shacklike wooden churches, one of them Roman Catholic "for the Mexicans." On the outskirts was a larger, spic-and-span church of white plaster roofed in red tile, a copy of an old Spanish mission, with a matching rectory. The "Community Church," Mrs. Ives called it, "where most of the winter people go. A minister lives here every winter."

Mrs. Ives also pointed out one or two more exotic institutions. There was a small whitewashed building with a bright blue dome — "The Mosque." It was a house, really, inhabited by two young Englishmen. "Remittance men," Mrs. Ives said they were. "Recluses. They wear beards and sandals. They're said to conduct Mohammedan services for themselves." The Bahai temple was larger, with landscaped grounds and bungalows where numbers of the faithful came now and again for sojourn and prayer. Mrs. Ives expressed amused tolerance of the mosque and the temple. "There's a lunatic fringe wherever you go in southern California. We say it's the price we have to pay for so much beauty."

At the far end of the valley, with a splendid view of the western mountain wall, we came to a boys' preparatory school. We drove through the grounds, past a group of boys on horseback — every boy had his own horse, I learned — but Mrs. Ives said we wouldn't "call on Dr. and Mrs. Tucker today." Some other day. And then we turned up a steep road and drove along a ledge, past the houses of some of Mrs. Ives's friends. She told me a little about each inhabitant, promising that I would soon be acquainted with them. As she described them, they were all elderly folk, chiefly widows or spinsters, whose "base residences" (Mrs. Ives's term) were in various of the colder areas of the United States or in Canada. "We come from many different places," she said, "but our backgrounds are congenial." That made me remember something Bob Ives had said to me — a warning, was it? "The landscape out there has a pagan beauty about it. But there's nothing pagan about the winter colony. And my aunt's very much one of the colony."

The sun was orange and close to the horizon, the shadows of the mountains were spreading across the valley floor, sky and snowfields beginning to take on evening color, when suddenly I learned that our ride had a definite objective. "If you'll turn into the next driveway on the right," said Mrs. Ives, "a few hundred yards ahead, that will be Miss Myers. I told her we might stop in for a cup of tea. She's president of the Women's Club this year, and she's eager to meet you. I think a few other ladies may be there, too. It's Club Day."

The look on Mrs. Ives's face betrayed her awareness of indulging in a bit of social trickery, and I couldn't help laughing. She smiled too. "Believe me if you can," she said, "I really planned it like this for your sake. It seemed to me a quick and easy way for you to meet my winter cronies and get it over with."

I have said that Mrs. Ives was tiny. As I stopped the car before Miss Myers', she noticed that one of her shoelaces was untied, and sitting there beside me in the front seat she bent down to tie it. In that position she was invisible to anyone who might open Miss Myers' door. Someone now did open it, from within. Someone tall and sharp-faced, wearing a Queen Mary toque and pince-nez. "Chauffeur!" this caricature screeched, in a cracked voice. "Chauffeur! Get away from there at once! No waiting there, you're blocking the view! Whoever you're waiting for, move further down where you belong!" She sounded demented. She pointed to a broader part of the drive-way, beyond, where a number of cars were parked. And then — without waiting to see whether I obeyed her command — as quickly as she had appeared, she withdrew, slamming the door behind her.

Mrs. Ives cast me a scandalized look from her crouched position, and she remained crouched until she heard the house-door close. When she straightened up, her cheeks were bright pink. "I'm so sorry," she said to me. "So very sorry. That was most unfortunate. I hope you don't think I was cowardly. I thought quickly, and decided I didn't want Maude to see me: she would have felt too badly about her mistake. She would have been mortified at having addressed a guest of mine as a servant. Let's not go in after all today."

"I'm quite willing to go in if you are. In fact I'd rather like to."

"No, it would be unkind. Maude would find out, and be mortified. Let's just drive home."

So homeward we drove. We were silent, Mrs. Ives doubtless continuing to deplore a social gaffe, and I biting my tongue lest I challenge what was apparently a way of life. When we were nearly home we exchanged a few remarks about the sunset, which was developing into a full-scale Maxfield Parrish affair, a worthy pendant to the sunrise that now seemed to have taken place long, long ago.

In the driveway of El Espolón a car was parked. "Oh dear," said Mrs. Ives. "Dr. Drace."

I left her at the path leading to the front door, and drove the Franklin down into the garage. The second overhead door was open, and the Ebbets' car was gone. In the house I found everything on the main floor dark except the entrance hall, and went to my room.

When I emerged for dinner, there was news. Mr. Ebbet's temperature had gone up a little. The doctor, called by Mrs. Ebbet, had come and sent June for a prescription. Mr. Ebbet must stay in bed until his temperature returned to normal. Even thereafter, the medication must be continued. It would probably cause dizziness. Mr. Ebbet must not drive.

"That part needn't inconvenience anybody," I said. "I can take over the driving perfectly well."

"Oh, no, you have your work. The Ebbets very generously offered to have June substitute for as long as necessary."

"Would you be easy with June at the wheel? Have you ever driven with her?" And when Mrs. Ives shook her head I said, "You'd better let me go out with her in the morning and see if she's a possibility."

"Oh, but you want to get started on your . . ."

"Even if she's good she'll want to get used to the Franklin."

"Well, I must say everybody's being very thoughtful."

June was a splendid driver. A little on the exuberant side — after we had driven a few miles I made her go back to the garage and begin all over again, pretending that Mrs. Ives was in the car — but always in control, and quick to catch on: the second drive was a model of even comfort. Mrs. Ives had said that since we were going out we might as well do some shopping, and at the Japanese market in Ventura we bought local fruit and vegetables, marvelously fresh and green in midwinter. A gray surf was pounding the beach, and crossing the highway we pushed against the wind along the boardwalk to a coffee stand. June had wrapped a pink scarf around her fair hair, and it combined with the wind to give a glow to her skin, which was fine and usually pale. Up until then we had been attending strictly to business, but at the counter I was able to decide that although she was not a beautiful or even a pretty girl — her features, especially her jaw, were overbold, lacking in delicacy — the bright hair and pale skin kept her from being plain. Nor was her face expressionless; yet some of the expressions that crossed it, and certain of her mannerisms, and her speaking voice as contrasted with her singing, were . . .

"This is the life!" she helped me by saying. "If the girls at Sam's could see me now!"

The poor little coffee stand, the deserted Ventura beach, drab Ventura itself, so near and yet so far in relation to the glamours of Hollywood to the south and Montecito's smartness a few miles north: if this was "the life" . . . ! Sam's, I learned, was the five-and-dime store of Randall, Indiana, population 22,000, and it was because of some "mix-up" at Sam's that June was here. "I wasn't fired" — self-esteem often took the form, in those Depression days, of not having been fired — "I just wanted to get away." As she spoke, I remembered a snobbish Frenchman I had known who had deplored the American bride chosen by one of his friends: *"Elle est très drugstore.*" That came close to describing June. Not *"très dimestore,"* perhaps, but *"un peu dimestore";* not big-city, not hopelessly dime-a-dance dimestore, but dimestore nonetheless.

Out in the wind again, on the way back to the car, she burst into song: "Button up your overcoat . . . Button up your overcoat . . ." On the empty boardwalk we did a few dance capers — separately — and then we got into the Franklin and she drove it sedately along the winding road inland to the valley.

Rounding one sharp curve she slowed down so ultraconsiderately that I laughed. "Don't let Mrs. Ives think you're making fun of her," I warned. "By the way" — June was smoking, and I opened one of the windows — "she may be going out with you this afternoon, and I'm sure she'd rather the car not be filled with cigarette smoke."

"You mean because she doesn't like smoke? Or are you talking about her not liking *me* to smoke?"

"Both."

June shrugged as she had the previous morning. "OK. But just for the first reason." She stubbed out her cigarette, and I detached the ashtray and emptied it out the window.

"What about smoking and singing, June?" I asked, when the air in the car had freshened a little. "Haven't other people talked to you about it? Teachers, and so on?"

"Plenty of them. And I'm sick of the subject. One of the last persons that mentioned it to me, I said, 'I know which I'd give up first,' and I meant it."

"Then you'd be giving up much the best thing about yourself," was what I came close to retorting. I wondered why she should have reacted so mutinously: as she spoke that way her jaw was particularly stiff and heavy. "A voice like yours is such a treat for everybody that I guess we almost think we have some rights in it ourselves," I said. "I was thinking of something else, too: you must look very well on a stage." It was easy, I found, to picture this blond girl in the limelight, flooding a theatre or an opera house with the lovely singing I had heard the previous morning.

"You mean I'd look all right from far enough away?"

There was something in that, though it was not entirely what I had meant, and of course I denied it.

Every day I went down to visit Mr. Ebbet for a few minutes, sometimes with Mrs. Ives, sometimes alone. The servants' rooms were below the kitchen, down a flight of back stairs that opened onto the driveway near the garage. They were heated not by the furnace that served the rest of the house, but by electric radiators. "Juice-eaters," Mrs. Ives called them one day, when she and I had returned upstairs after our visit to the sickroom. The slang sounded comical on her tongue. "Juice-eaters — it was never supposed that either of those rooms would have to be heated so continuously."

Mr. Ebbet did not look badly. His neat, small-featured clerk's face was rosy against the white pillows, and the same good color showed even through the thin hair on the top of his head. "I see you have moved the two beds apart," Mrs. Ives remarked to Mrs. Ebbet one day. "Is it more convenient so?"

"Yes. I hope you don't mind. All the tucking-in and straightening . . ."

Both Ebbets thanked me for my "coaching" of June at the wheel of the Franklin. She was driving it regularly now, down to the village for morning shopping and the mail, and with Mrs. Ives on what I learned were the regular weekly big-shopping, meat-buying expeditions to "Santa B." On Sundays she drove Mrs. Ives to the Community Church: the Ebbets themselves, Mrs. Ives told me, had found in one of the smaller churches an approximation of the sect they belonged to in Indiana.

Occasionally, in the afternoon, after stopping my own work for the day, I drove Mrs. Ives out on a sight-seeing or social expedition. We attended one of the Women's Club teas, the hostess this time being Mrs. Tucker, at the Headmaster's House of the Tucker School. There were a dozen or so hatted ladies present, including Miss Myers, whose voice cracked toward me today in the kindest of welcomes. Dr. Tucker himself bustled in toward the end, a gentleman of seventy or so wearing plus-fours and carrying a briefcase: his wife murmured to those nearest her that he was just back from an emergency trip to Los Angeles. After greeting each of us and inviting me cordially to come up with Mrs. Ives for dinner "in hall" one evening and give a little talk to the boys — "We don't often hear a voice from Gotham" — he cleared his throat in a way that was recognized as a signal, and made an announcement. "I must tell you that we have found poor Mr. Wiman at last."

I knew who Mr. Wiman was. Several times lately Mrs. Ives had mentioned the missing music teacher. A fortnight earlier he had gone East to be present at the deathbed and funeral of his father in Maine, and although from there he had promptly telegraphed the date of his return, that date had come and gone without him. His car, which he had left at the station in Pasadena when he had boarded the eastbound Chief, was not there when the police sought it at Dr. Tucker's request.

"I received a call from the Los Angeles police this morning," Dr. Tucker now told us all, "and I went down at once. I know how sorry you will be to hear that poor Mr. Wiman was found last night wandering the streets of Los Angeles in a daze. It has been diagnosed as amnesia. Mr. Wiman is a very sick man, and will be for some time. There is no question of his returning to teach this year. We did the only thing we could — telephoned his brother in Boston. He will come out and take him East for the long rest and treatment he needs. It's a sad, sad story."

The gasps that had greeted the earlier part of the announcement gave way to a general murmur, and one lady cried, "Oh, Dr. Tucker, do tell us which hospital the poor lad is in. Some of his friends here must certainly drive down and try to cheer him up."

"Cheer him up! My dear lady! He would not recognize you. He is in no condition to receive visitors, I assure you. And besides, as I said, in a few days he will be gone."

The tea party broke up rather quickly after the tragic news.

"Oh dear," Mrs. Ives lamented, on our way home, "why did it have to be Mr. Wiman? He was such a fine young man."

"You may not have to say 'was,'" I pointed out. "Amnesia victims often recover completely. He may well be back next year as good as ever."

"I do hope so. He was such an asset at church: he played the organ for us on Sundays. I was looking forward to your knowing him. In fact, Mr. Wiman was *the* young person I had to offer you, here in the valley. The rest of Dr. Tucker's faculty is older generation, like all of us. He told us once he's come to prefer it that way, because young instructors so often, so very often nowadays, seem to develop problems. I can't think why. It's so serene here."

Mrs. Ives had also looked forward to getting Mr. Wiman's opinion on June's voice, she told me. "I had great confidence in his taste" — she persisted in speaking of him as though he were dead — "and he might have had ideas about how she should practice. What a loss he is!"

Even without Mr. Wiman's advice, June was practicing regularly. I suppose Mrs. Ives was thinking that Mrs. Ebbet wasn't the most accomplished or professional of coaches, and she was probably right; however, almost every day after lunch the aunt and the niece had their music hour at Mrs. Ives's piano. Mrs. Ives would shut her door, I would make myself invisible somewhere, and the two ladies would emerge from the kitchen with their sheet music and begin. They had various ways of warming up. Sometimes June would break into unaccompanied scales and roulades — there were always plenty of those anyway, interspersed among the songs; sometimes they played a kind of follow-the-leader game, with Mrs. Ebbet rippling up and down the piano, seemingly at random, and June racing vocally after; or they might begin with one or two popular songs, anything from "The Rosary" to "I Can't Give You Anything but Love, Baby." Sometimes there would be what they called a "ballad," usually well-known lines of English verse — "Have you seen but a bright lily grow," or "Come into the garden, Maud" — set to music that was often less distinguished. But sooner or later they would tackle June's big-number repertory. This consisted of two French arias, the "Mohn Koor" I had heard her sing the first morning, and another that also sounded like Saint-Saëns but was unfamiliar to me, and not, from June's diction, identifiable.

I was no Mr. Wiman, but to me June's voice seemed from the beginning to be a marvel: its beauty was so great, and of so many shades. From the sweetest, freshest, lightest high notes she could sink to tones so deep and majestic that their very sound, unconnected with the sense of any words, evoked nothing less than the grandeur of ceremony or tragedy. It was uncanny to feel the color of one's thoughts controlled by the sounds that poured almost casually from the throat of this young girl. Nevertheless, the more I heard June sing, especially when she practiced her two French arias, the more I thought that even I could give her, on one score, a little counsel.

One day, when I was particularly tempted to interfere, telepathy occurred, the transmitter being Mrs. Ives. "Mrs. Ebbet noticed that you've been reading a French book. She asked me whether you'd be willing to give June a few hints." Just that afternoon it had dawned on me that the mysterious opening words of the unfamiliar song — "*Prin tempse quee commencee*," as sung by June — were "*Printemps qui commence*," which I now remembered as being indeed the title of another aria from *Samson and Delilah*. What set me onto it was the difficulty June was having with the final "ee": it was half strangling her each time she sang it, and it was only one of several such troublesome misreadings.

So began a series of little "*leçons de français*," as June was soon calling them in quite a respectable accent — half indoors, half out to take advantage of a spell of beautiful weather which after a week of rain had come over all of southern California and was particularly brilliant in the valley. Mrs. Ives called it "treacherous," and refused to go out except bundled in woolens and even in furs, but June and I reveled in it. After lunch while Mrs. Ives napped we would come and go through the French doors, carrying each group of newly learned French phrases with us, so to speak, from the hot glare of the patio where we had been saying them over and over, to be tried out at the piano in the living room, shuttered, cavernous by contrast. Each time, June was newly incredulous at the vocal ease the new pronunciation brought. "Why, French can sing as smooth as English! I'd just as soon sing '*Mon coeur s'ouvre*' as 'Mean to Me'!"

June's lovely voice, singing a phrase of Saint-Saëns —

> *A la nuit tomban-te*
> *J'irai, triste aman-te . . .*

cast a fantastic spell of old-fashioned French operatic romance. While she sang she was transfigured and I was transported: there was no need to close my eyes to imagine myself far from this California valley, at the Opéra, listening to a Gallic diva of the last century, draped and mascaraed, in private life possibly the mistress of a Maupassantian character grown rich on the Bourse; and underlying the exotic illusion was the authority, the actual sensual beauty of the voice — it's not too much to say that I felt a love for it, as I think almost any man, and woman too, would have felt, as long as it was pulsing, hovering there in the air. I was at the feet of this singer, one of her audience, shouting "Brava!" And the next moment, the song over, the spell was shattered, and suddenly before me stood the high school girl, the dimestore girl, teasing: "Gee, I'm dying for a cigarette." June smoked so constantly that a cigarette often burned in an ashtray on the piano as she sang, waiting to be taken up again. Part of her lesson equipment was her apron: at the end, on her aunt's orders, she ran about the living room flapping it, to clear the air for Mrs. Ives.

Apart from the smoking, June was cooperative during the lessons. She hadn't spoken disparagingly of her voice since the day of our drive to Ventura, and she practiced enthusiastically.

I made translations for her, writing them under the French words on the score, for I had found that she had had almost as little idea of the separate meanings of the words she had been singing as of their proper sound. But I couldn't tell whether she was pretending or not when she exclaimed in surprise at the sentiments revealed.

> *Ainsi qu'on voit des blés les épis onduler*
> Just as we see the wheatstalks wave
> *Sous la brise légère,*
> Under the gentle breeze,
> *Ainsi frémit mon coeur, prêt à se consoler*
> So quivers my heart, longing to be eased,
> *A ta voix qui m'est chère.*
> At the sound of your dear voice.

"Gee! Does it really say that? I'll be darned! Hot stuff!"

"You're beginning to sing it as though you really meant it, June," I remarked one day.

"Maybe I do mean it. At least I know now what *it* means."

"Why these particular songs, June? Two arias from the same opera. Did you choose them yourself?"

"They're an assignment."

The accompanying look dared me to question further.

"The sheet music," I pointed out, "comes from France."

"I know it does.

> *'How yah gonna keep 'em down on the farm,*
> *After they've seen Paree? . . .'* "

I joined in, and we sang it through together. June stretched and yawned in the hot sun, pulling her jumper tight over the front of her body, exhaling a tremendous lungful of smoke. "Smell those California smells! If the girls at Sam's could see me now!"

Sage grew wild in crevices below the rim of Mrs. Ives's rocky spur; the hot sun drew out its aromatic tang and was opening the buds on the orange trees farther down the slope; the walls of the patio itself were festooned with jasmine, much visited by hummingbirds. June reached out and caught one, one day, just like that, with a quick gesture as though plucking a grape from the air. She held it cupped in her hand for a moment, trembling and iridescent, then kissed it and let it go. "*Colibri*": she sang the word to an improvised little phrase after I said it to her. "*Colibri*."

Her lips, that had just kissed the bird, were not far from mine as she sang "*Colibri, colibri*," and as we looked into each other's eyes I knew what she was waiting for. I had seldom heard anything sweeter, or more touching, than June spontaneously singing "*Colibri, colibri*," in that voice of hers, and the next moment I would certainly have kissed her, if we hadn't heard someone coming. Mrs. Ebbet appeared, as she did now and then. She was in her housedress, holding a dish towel. "I've been listening to you — quite the French class. Sounds wonderful to me. Isn't the air grand? Well, I must get back to my sink." I was becoming vaguely aware that Mrs. Ebbet seemed always to be washing dishes.

June ran after her and flapped her apron around the living room. The lesson was over.

One day a great morning freshness and fragrance poured into my room, woke me, filled me with high spirits, and urged me up and out, for the first time, well before breakfast. From the loggia, through the French doors, I saw June in the patio. Her hair was wrapped in a bandanna and she was waltzing with a broom. By breakfast time the front of the house was always dusted and the patio swept, but I hadn't realized that since her uncle's illness June had taken over this work as well as the driving. I stood watching, and was just about to go out and greet her when the bedroom hall door behind me opened and Mrs. Ives emerged. I put my finger to my lips and beckoned, and she came and stood beside me. June and her broom were revolving slowly, and she was humming softly, just too softly for me to know what. Mrs. Ives watched for a moment, and then, with a peculiar, very brief glance at me — I felt that the glance was directed, more precisely, at my *watching* — she said, "Indeed!" and moved on. A moment later I heard her and Mrs. Ebbet exchange good-mornings in the kitchen.

I went out through one of the French doors, greeted June, and said, "Give me that broom." She laughed: I think she supposed for a moment that I wanted to dance with it. I held out my hand. "Give over."

Her expression changed. "No, no."

"Yes. Give it to me. I'll sweep. You dust."

"Are you crazy?" She swung away and began to sweep hard, raising a cloud of dust. When I shrank back from the dust, my angry little game was over before it began. I walked out into the narrow strip of garden and stared at the mountains, their outline blurred against the sun that was bright above them. June must have scanted her job that morning: I didn't stare at the mountains very long, and when I turned back she was gone.

At breakfast Mrs. Ives told me in a low voice that Mr. Ebbet's temperature was not subsiding as the doctor had hoped, and that Mrs. Ebbet had just declared that she and her husband were "embarrassed" at the situation in which they found themselves. Dr. Drace wanted Mr. Ebbet to stay in bed. "But the very realization that we're imposing on you, and not doing our job, is fretting him, and the doctor says fretting is the worst thing he can do," Mrs. Ebbet had said. Mrs. Ives had gone downstairs and "scolded" Mr. Ebbet, and he had promised to "behave." The Ebbets had then suggested that Mrs. Ives put them temporarily on half wages, but, "Under the circumstances, I told them I wouldn't consider it," Mrs. Ives reported. Whether by "circumstances" she was referring chiefly to the Ebbets' burden of medical expense, or to the fact that with June doing the driving and the cleaning the Ebbet family was providing just about full service anyway, was not clear: June was mentioned by neither of us.

The conversation, or rather Mrs. Ives's breakfast monologue — she was talking rather compulsively this morning — then turned to some news she had gleaned at the most recent tea party. The Roosevelt Administration — it was just beginning to be called the New Deal — had recently organized the agency called the Civilian Conservation Corps to provide work for unemployed young people, and I learned now what I had not known before: that a tract of government land in the valley, not far from the Tucker School, had been picked as the site of one of the CCC camps. Mrs. Ives assured me that "DFR" (that was the customary way she and her friends referred to the president. "Not FDR," they sometimes specified, "but DFR") had done this "personally, because he knows what kind of people we are here." Some "young toughs from the Chicago slums" had already arrived in army trucks and were living in tents, under the orders of an army colonel and a government forester. At present they were setting up barracks. Once housed, they would "supposedly" work in the National Forest, improving trails, making firebreaks, removing dead timber. "Heaven knows what they will really be up to." The tea party news was that the colonel had driven over to see Dr. Tucker, introduced himself, and made an unofficial request. The recent rains had left the camp site a morass, he said, and though the mud was being coped with in various ways, ball games and other sports were temporarily impossible. He asked Dr. Tucker whether, "as a morale-booster," until the camp site was drained, the CCC men might use the school ball field and track for an hour or so of recreation at the end of each day. He had noticed that there was an hour's daylight left, these days, after the Tucker boys went indoors. "He guaranteed perfect maintenance," Mrs. Ives told me, "and offered landscaping services to the school in return for the favor. Dr. Tucker said the colonel himself was a perfect gentleman, but naturally he had to decline. He pointed out that his students had been entrusted to his care by their parents, and he had no right to expose them to risky contacts. As he said to us — I don't know whether he put it quite this way to the colonel — 'Boys from the sort of families ours belong to have nothing to learn from those other elements. It's all the other way.'"

And Mrs. Ives went on, after an almost imperceptible pause, as though the subject were being changed, "By the way, I hope June is profiting from your French lessons?"

"She is," I answered. "What did the colonel say?"

"Dr. Tucker didn't tell us, but I suppose . . ." Mrs. Ives broke off, and did not resume.

Was I wrong in the fancy I had? I fancied that Mrs. Ives wanted to say, "I suppose the colonel told Dr. Tucker he was quite right," but that despite her loyalty to her fellow valley-dwellers and their code she was kept silent by the generosity of her spirit — it was greater, I suspected, than that of most of her neighbors, and proof of it was the presence of June and me in her house.

"As to June," I said, "I think she's a good girl, and that you shouldn't worry about her."

This time I didn't have to have a fancy. This time Mrs. Ives's answer, unspoken, but expressed in a glance, was unquestionably: "Maybe, but do I have to worry about *you?*"

I learned the truth about Mr. Wiman in the barbershop, one afternoon a few days later when the air over the valley was heavy with the scent of the blossoming orange groves.

"Mr. Ives always thought it was better to go over to Santa B., to the barber in the Biltmore," Mrs. Ives had warned me, when I said I was going to walk down to the village for a haircut; and indeed the shabby little local establishment bore every mark, as I approached it, of not enjoying genteel patronage. An empty black car from a neighboring town — the words "Oxnard Taxi" were painted in white on its two front doors — was parked outside. Within, I found that I was in no mere barbershop. The place smelled as much of wine as of hair lotion, and standing about were several thick white china coffee cups, stained with a color not that of coffee. Cups were the tribute conventionally paid to Prohibition, which was still with us, but the candor of the little speakeasy anticipated Repeal. I found the barber pursuing both sides of his business: a rugged-looking customer was holding a white china cup while under the clippers.

After both men greeted me — one via the mirror — and looked me over, and found me a stranger, a conversation I had interrupted was resumed while I read a newspaper. "I know what he wanted," the barber said. "One last bellyful of grass before coming back to the dry corral. It's natural. What happened? One of those L.A. girls working with the police? That's how I got it from a kitchen help at the school."

"You got it turned around. The cops were out for the girl because she hadn't been splitting. They were watching her, and as soon as she took him upstairs they walked in."

"How come Doc got you to drive him down? I should have thought he'd like to handle it private."

"He didn't know what was waiting for him. On the phone they told him one of his men was sick and needed help. For all he knew, we might have to carry him. He almost hired an ambulance."

"Were they holding the girl too?"

"They didn't ever bring her in — she paid up on the spot. I guess he wishes he'd done the same. He'd still be working. As it was, when he put up an argument they just held him a few days. Then they called Doc to come and get him. That way they made sure he'd lose his job *and* his car. He was broke. The son of the sergeant bought the car. His father said he was looking for a nice one cheap, and he *got* a nice one cheap. Paid just enough for it to cover a Santa Fe ticket East after the fine."

"Fornication?"

"No — that's a crime. They agreed to make it vagrancy — a misdemeanor — when Doc cried about the school's good name. Anybody in the valley swallowing the amnesia story?"

"Even the old biddies on the ridge are onto the facts by now."

I kept my eyes on my newspaper. The revelation was disconcerting: apparently I'd been more naïve than the old biddies.

There was more regional gossip, none of which meant anything to me. The taxi driver had his cup refilled from some keg or jug in a back room, then his sheet was stripped from him and he left, nodding to me and handing the barber a dollar bill — thirty-five cents for the haircut, a quarter a cup for the wine, and "keep the change."

As I replaced him on the still-warm seat, the barber eyed me more closely: perhaps he was beginning to think he'd seen me around, or perhaps he was just studying me professionally. "Anything else?" he suggested, when I asked for my badly needed trim. I said "I wouldn't mind," and in a moment I was discovering the wine to be surprisingly good. "There's nothing like hearing a story from the absolute horse's mouth," he declared, as he set to work. His tone betrayed the pryer and pumper, but it was easy to switch the talk to the wine. It came from near San Francisco. "Tremendous things" were going on at the wineries, the barber said, in preparation for Repeal. "Have you seen the vineyards? Up there grapes are like citrus here, all the country's vines. Sometimes I shut my eyes and think of those millions of gallons of the purple stuff all ready to flood out over the country. A person with my little sideline might resent Repeal, but I take a bigger view — there's a lot more of the purple stuff available, thank God, than people like me can handle."

Eventually I left the bacchic barber, handing him a dollar bill — thirty-five cents for the haircut, a quarter a cup for the wine, and "keep the change."

Looking down on the floor of the valley as I climbed back up the ridge through the perfumed air, I saw that the powdering on the orange trees was grayed, like snow that was slightly passé; Mrs. Ives's grove, higher up, was in fresh white flower. Overhead, preparations were under way for one of the sunset spectaculars. As I approached the house I heard the piano, and June singing. I recognized the music of one of her ballads, "The Fair Singer," and I waited in the loggia, listening to her sing Marvell's words:

> *That, while she with her eyes my heart does bind,*
> *She with her voice might captivate my mind.*

Was that song an "assignment," too? Was there someone who felt that way about June? As for me, my mind and everything else about me continued to be enthralled by this fair singer when she sang; but as to the difference it made when she stopped . . . Something was troubling me, and I wasn't sure whether it was the difference, or the possibility that the difference was diminishing. Or a little of both.

From the authoritative accompaniment, I supposed that Mrs. Ebbet had been playing for her niece, but on entering the living room I saw that it was Mrs. Ives at the piano. June's surprised glance when she saw me come in quickly changed to the sidewise, puzzled look she had had for me since the episode of the broom. We had had no lesson since then: each day she had had after-lunch errands to do for Mrs. Ives in the village. "June's French is lovely now," Mrs. Ives said to me, composedly. "We've been going over her other songs, too. I've been telling her I want my friends to hear her beautiful voice. You know I'm having a few ladies to lunch tomorrow. After our coffee June has consented to sing. Shall we do one more now, June? Which shall it be?"

I left them, to go into the kitchen. At the table sat Mrs. Ebbet in an apron, her elbows on the white metal top, her handkerchief to her eyes. She heard me and sprang up, red-eyed. "Excuse me, oh, excuse me!"

"Can I do something?"

"No, no, what can *I* do? What would you like? What was it you wanted?"

"A glass of ice water. I'm so sorry . . ."

"It's nothing. It's just that Junie's voice is so lovely . . ." Her voice broke, and she got me the water.

"How is Mr. Ebbet?"

She sobbed. "Dr. Drace was here a little earlier . . ." She shook her head, tears welled over.

Mrs. Ives struck opening chords. *"Now sleeps the crimson petal,"* sang June, *"now the white . . ."*

Mrs. Ebbet tightened her lips, looked away, mastered herself. "When we sent for Junie to come out here we hoped to keep her busy through the winter, and then we planned when Mrs. Ives went back to Seattle in the spring, to take her up there with us and try to find her a scholarship in some music school. But now we all have to go back East."

"East? To Indiana? That climate? I should think that for Mr. Ebbet . . ."

"The sanatorium's there — the Indiana state san he was in before. That's why he had to stop work, you know — he wasn't fired. What he has now is a recurrence — there's no hiding it any longer. You probably guessed it anyway."

I should have, I supposed. Mr. Ebbet's coughing and fever and medication, the moving apart of the beds, all the dishwashing . . . It made me feel naïve, as when the barber had mentioned Mr. Wiman and the old biddies. There seemed to be so many things I wasn't onto — things in myself among them.

"The doctors at the san said he could work in a mild climate, so we came out and took what we could find. But I guess they were overoptimistic. Still, it's not us I feel sick about. It's June. With such a gift . . ."

"But she says she has no interest in a singing career."

"She has no real interest in the man she's sure to marry once she gets back home. That's worse. No sooner did we leave her behind when we came out here, than he went after her harder than ever, just what we were afraid of. Mrs. Ives allowed us to send for her. He's sincerely crazy about her, crazy about her voice, it kills him to see her smoke, he's very artistic, goes to Europe a lot — he chose those songs she practices, about the only ones she *will* practice — she says she might as well learn them for him since she'll probably marry him in the end. He's got plenty of money. I suppose if a girl has no particular goal in life it's hard for her to see why she shouldn't marry the boss."

"The boss? Sam?"

Mrs. Ebbet showed no surprise that I should know. "Mr. Samuels. Of Sam's. Yes. June always did have a taste for older men. But not that old — Mr. Samuels is very nice, but he must be sixty. It was men around your age she always liked when she was in high school. She tended to fling herself at them.

Maybe Mrs. Ives told you we were a little worried when we heard you were coming. We couldn't foresee you'd be such a gentleman."

Mrs. Ives easily acquiesced when I begged off joining her and her lady guests for lunch. This seemed a good day for a tramp up into the hills, where I had not yet ventured very far. Mrs. Ebbet said she'd make me sandwiches to take along. Mrs. Ebbet was obviously all "for" me: not only because I was such a gentleman, but also because I had promised to cooperate with her by keeping mum, for the moment, about the impending departures. "You caught me unawares, and I had to spill it," she said to me, "but I don't want to break the news even to Mr. Ebbet until tomorrow's guests have left. Discussing it will make me go to pieces, I know, and everybody will be upset. Mrs. Ives is so anxious to have the lunch just right."

When I sought out Mrs. Ives, midmorning, to tell her I was off, I found her directing June beside a sunny window in the living room. The pair of tall Chinese *sang de boeuf* vases that ordinarily adorned the mantelpiece had been taken down, and June, her hair done up in a cloth again, and rhythmically chewing gum, was rinsing and wiping them with a rag wrung out from a pail. I had always admired the two long-necked porcelain masterpieces, and now the gleam of sun and water on the ruby glaze was turning them into rivals of the valley sunsets and the one dawn I had seen. Mrs. Ives stroked the vase she held in her lap. "These things always seem to me so stalwart, so . . . masculine," she remarked. "I've always wondered why they call them oxblood, not bull's-blood." June's attention was certainly not caught by anything to do with Chinese porcelain, but it was caught: after all, she was a country girl. Her eyes met mine for a moment; her chewing slowed down. She looked away.

The mantelpiece was rather high. Folding steps had been brought out to enable June to reach it, and now I replaced one vase for her and waited for the other. "I think you told me once that a number of other people in Seattle have good

Chinese things like yours," I said to Mrs. Ives. "Was there a particular supply where they all came from?"

"Oh, yes. That is, there was one person, a remarkable man, who came to live in Seattle and had an influence on all of us. He opened our eyes to beautiful things. It was thanks to him that dealers from San Francisco made trips to Seattle with their trunks, in those early days, and we could buy. It was all due to him. He became quite well known in New York art circles later. I won't mention his name."

Probably Mrs. Ives would have gone on even without my puzzled glance. She waited until I had lifted the second vase onto the mantel, and June had left the room, carrying the pail back to the kitchen. I folded the steps and stood holding them, waiting to ask where they should go. "It ended unpleasantly. I was a young woman — it was my first disillusionment. We discovered that his lovely wife, whom we had all taken to our hearts, wasn't his wife at all, but somebody else's. Of course they had to move away."

"Of course," I thought. A sense of suffocation came over me, and I felt the urge to test the barber's confidence in the acuteness of the old biddies. "Poor Mr. Wiman," I murmured, as though irrelevantly.

Mrs. Ives glanced at me and flushed. She stood up and moved rapidly toward the door. "'Poor' Mr. Wiman no doubt," she said, as she crossed the room. "But knowing what we know now, I must say it would make me uncomfortable to see him playing the organ in church."

In the hills the quiet was delicious, the air brilliant, aromatic. Marked trails led in various directions. I climbed the steepest, up and up until live oak and olive and grass gave way to scrub, higher still without looking around, until I suspected it was time: I turned, and there it was, the Pacific, silver-blue beyond the coastal hills. Under a bush I rested on powdery, reddish earth. Mrs. Ives had insisted that I carry rattlesnake serum, but I saw nothing more alarming than a lizard. All was quiet except for the twittering of invisible birds.

About the time Mrs. Ives's guests were arriving I ate my sandwiches, then read a little and stretched out flat. I had been in the valley about a month. Now, I knew, my visit was almost over. If Mrs. Ives asked me to stay on for a while, after the Ebbets left, to be with her during the changeover to whatever the new regime might be, I would; but otherwise there was good reason for me to go. I had finished a few samples of work, and quite apart from being ready to try my luck in the marketplace I was feeling dissatisfied and restless. Not *vaguely* dissatisfied and restless: I knew why. Mrs. Ives's and Mrs. Ebbet's fears had been more justified than they knew. It hadn't turned out well that June and I should be in the same house. A nice dimestore girl and "such a gentleman" made an uneasy combination, after all.

In the dappled shade I dozed off and slept an hour or more. Then a clatter woke me, and I sat up in time to see a pair of white-tailed deer rushing down the slope below me. Stones dislodged by their hooves were rattling after them: they must have caught sight of me as they browsed, and fled in panic. I rose and wandered a bit higher in this upland wilderness, climbing until far below there appeared the sandy line of a stretch of coast — I suppose between Ventura and Santa Barbara; then I headed downhill, like the deer. Already shadows were lengthening. Here and there I noticed catlike footprints embedded in the earth, dating doubtless from the last damp weather. Mountain lions roamed the hills, I had been told, but I saw none now.

What I did see, after a little while, in the distance, was a line of human figures descending another trail. There was a far sound of singing. The troop kept disappearing from view as our trails zigzagged, and then would reappear, each time a little closer. The singing grew steadily louder, until I recognized the tune of "Carry Me Back to Ole Virginny." Then a few words reached me — "Carry me back to ole *Chicago*": the rest I couldn't catch. I knew whom I was running into, of course, even before I saw the army fatigue clothes and the shovels, picks, and machetes the boys were carrying.

Carry me back to ole Chicago,
That's where the asphalt and the fun and floosies grow . . .

Our trails were coming very close, but the others were momentarily invisible behind live oaks when the singing suddenly diminished, and against the background of one or two persistent singers I heard cries. "Oboyoboy . . . Do you see what I see? . . . Yippee! . . ." And one falsetto "*Look* at those lovely oranges!"

The next moment there was a three-way confrontation — a one hundred percent Depression-born confrontation, it occurred to me — at the fork of the trails. My appearance momentarily silenced the troop; then, among a chorus of "Hi's," came a partial resumption of banter: "Where did you come from, baby dear? . . . Buenas tardes, delicious." June, ascending, had stepped off the trail, pressing against a clump of bushes to let the troop pass down. He head was up in an attitude of high school disdain, but her eyes were flickering over the troop and toward me. I went over and put an arm around her shoulders while returning the "Hi's." The boys were dirt-streaked, sweat-soaked, smelly, very young, grinning, and — touchingly — respectful of my possessive gesture. "On your way, men!" a voice called, and with a rumble of groans the troop resumed its way down the trail. "No luck today," one hollow voice loudly intoned, and echoes of "No luck today" gradually turned into a reprise of the theme song: "Carry me back to ole Chicago . . ."

"What are you doing, walking in the woods by yourself?" I asked June. "It's not a good idea, especially at this time of day."

I was thinking of mountain lions, but she answered, "Oh, those kids, who cares about them?"

My arm dropped from her shoulders, she lit a cigarette. True to form, I pointed to the yellow "No Smoking, National Forest" sign a yard away, and she put it out. "What have you got on under that pullover?" she asked, with a giggle. "Nothing at all?"

"How did the concert go?" I asked her. "Did the ladies

appreciate it?" I made as though to move off along the trail, but June sat down.

"Uh-huh. One of them said she could get me a scholarship in Minneapolis, or someplace. Somebody in her family's a trustee of something."

"Are you going to take it?"

She shook her head. "You know I'm not. You know what's happening to us — to me. My aunt told us, you know."

"You could still go to Minneapolis."

June shrugged, lit another cigarette, glanced at the sign, and continued smoking. "I knew you'd be coming down the trail. I came out to tell you we're leaving next week at the latest. They're breaking the news to Mrs. Ives now."

We were silent. Then, "Come on, June. Let's go," I said. "The light will start failing before we know it."

She laid a hand on the grass beside her. Invisible wires were pulling me down, but I was pulling backward, and I knew I'd win — if you call it winning.

"You sure look cute in that pullover."

Why wasn't it I who was saying something like that? "See you later, June," I said. "Be sure to rub out your cigarette."

I started down, ready to turn back if I heard nothing, but before long I heard her coming after.

That is what I was like in those days. And with a great feeling of malaise along with it. It seems to me now that I must have been looking at June and myself as though from between a pair of blinkers that cut off much that was real: she wasn't the kind of girl I'd ever gone with or ever wanted to go with — therefore I couldn't possibly be wanting to go with her now. Perhaps the winter people's snobbery had made me "kinder" to her than I might have been, while blinding me to my own snobbery, and perhaps this "kindness" of mine misled her. Her youth and spirits, her presence, these contrasted with the old age, the puritanism and ghastly hypocrisy around us. But not even the dryness of the corral quite drove me to want this nice little dimestore girl badly enough; even the pact I had made to stay away from her didn't propel me toward her; not even the compliments, so close to taunts, on being a "gentleman." Any real involvement with June might well have become a worry, even a tragedy, for both of us; but except when she sang, and at moments like that of her dance with the broom, or just now beside the trail, when I all but had the feel of her in my arms, I seldom had to remind myself of the danger.

Mrs. Ives, I found at dinner that night, had quickly decided not to look for replacements for the Ebbets, but to close El Espolón for the rest of the season. Friends in La Jolla and San Diego had been inviting her to visit, and after leaving them she would return to Seattle early, in time to "see the bulbs" in her northern garden for the first time in years. It was easy for me to set her mind at rest when she apologized for cutting short my stay. Clearly she was not grief stricken to part from the Ebbets, sorry though she was for their predicament. "There's nothing so comfortable as good, old-fashioned *professional* servants," she said.

After dinner we went downstairs to see the patient. His temperature was intermittent, he rarely coughed. Nowadays, I suppose, instead of being driven more than halfway across the continent to a sanatorium, he would be given different drugs, taken out of bed, and encouraged to lead a quiet, normal life. Assuming all else to be equal, Mrs. Ives would be able to keep her house open, and June would be spared the need to return — at least, to return so quickly — to Randall, Indiana, and to —.

And to Mr. Samuels, I suppose. Did she ever become Mrs. Samuels? Is she Mrs. Samuels now? I never heard what became of any of the Ebbets, though I corresponded with Mrs. Ives until her death a few years later.

Up to the moment of my departure from the valley, June kept sending out her signals. Before breakfast on my last morning I walked out into the patio, where she had just finished sweeping. We stood for a moment looking out at the mountains beyond and the lush valley below, its floor striped for miles with row upon row of orange and lemon trees, now once again entirely green. I said I knew I'd miss the place.

"I'll miss some things about it," June said.

"There hasn't been much here for you to miss."

"Oh, I'll miss the sunshine. I'll miss being out West. And Mrs. Ives has been really kind — I'll miss her. And —"

Her last word was uttered in a lower voice. Nevertheless, I heard it quite well. It was "you." I felt my heart turn over — with homage, even with love. We were silent, her tribute hovering between us. Why didn't I reach out and grasp it, as she had plucked the hummingbird out of the air? I had to deal with her somehow. The scenery — the glorious panorama that had been a scapegoat on my very first morning in the valley — now played that role again. "Yes," I said, *the view.* I was inexorable, God help me. "The view is certainly superb."

(1964)

Soirée
à la Chandelle

From her bed, Mrs. Curtius could look out into the salon of the hotel suite. Directly, she saw little of the salon itself, but within her line of vision was the high mirror over the white marble mantelpiece, and in that, reflected, was much of the rest of the room and the people in it. Beyond (for all the rooms of this old-fashioned Paris hotel were communicating, *en enfilade*, as in French palaces), she could even catch a glimpse, through a half-opened door, of part of her daughter's room; and beyond that, she knew but could not see, was her son's. Her son and daughter were in the salon now, talking in low voices and finishing, with Mademoiselle Rémy, the night nurse, an after-dinner bottle of champagne.

For, since her recent arrival in Paris, Mrs. Curtius had fallen prey to a weakness, of undetermined origin, which came on her most strongly at night, and though the doctors whom she had perforce consulted, and who were "observing" and "making tests," had urged her to move to a *clinique* or to the American Hospital, she was clinging to the living arrangements already made for this Parisian stay that had come to her like the most unexpected of gifts. Neither her son nor her daughter was young, could possibly be considered anything less than middle-aged, and yet here were Rose, and Tom, and she herself, "still able to totter," as she was apt to say, visiting Paris blessedly together again, just the three of them, as they so often had when she herself was a young widow with two teen-agers to bring abroad. All the present teen-agers, her grandchildren, and their other two parents, were busy at one thing or another back home — it was surprising how many teen-agers and older-agers didn't even want to come to Paris for a few weeks anymore — and to be one of the old threesome again was so blissful, so gratuitous, that she would literally, she told herself, prefer to break it up only by dying, if she had to, rather than by moving out of it to please a doctor.

And about this happiness that had come to her there was unquestionably something unreal, something dreamlike; it was a mother's dream come true, only she couldn't always credit the truth of it — especially, often, as twilight deepened, as now, and as with night came the feebleness, the intermittent faintness, that was puzzling the doctors and that had forced her to engage old Mademoiselle Rémy.

"We really should start if we're to get into the Louvre," she could hear Rose saying, in the salon. "The night-lighting in the Greek rooms began ten minutes ago, and everybody says they crowd up impossibly."

Tom answered something about his feet maybe not being up to the Greek rooms after all, considering the "stroll" — he emphasized the word ironically — the two of them had taken through the Marais that afternoon. Mrs. Curtius smiled as she heard him add — it was almost as though he had raised his voice for her benefit — "Sometimes I like to imagine that Mother catches her night weakness from us — all this daytime retracing of old footsteps we're doing for her."

Out of courtesy to Mademoiselle Rémy they spoke in

French, a second language to both of them, and Mademoiselle Rémy had just commented, with Gallic dutifulness, *"Il paraît que l'illumination des salles du Louvre est un spectacle absolument féerique,"* when all the lights abruptly went out. All the lights in the suite, at least, including the little lamp on Mrs. Curtius' night table.

As she heard steps quickly approach her door and then go quietly away again when she breathed deeply, pretending sleep, in answer to the nurse's soft question, *"Tout va bien, Madame?"* she could see, looking out the tall, open, fourth-floor windows, that in the eighteenth-century mansions across the rue de Lille there were lights in the façades and in the courtyards, and even some greenish glimmerings in the almost hidden gardens — lighted dining tables, perhaps, under the trees. In the salon, conversation had stopped; and the quiet, and the sudden deep twilight of the rooms that now matched the color of the Paris evening outside, abruptly created so serene, so poignantly pleasant an atmosphere that Mrs. Curtius wondered: "Why don't we sometimes just turn out the lights ourselves, and enjoy the gathering darkness, since it's as charming as this when it's imposed on us?"

"Mademoiselle Rémy," she heard Rose ask, "has anyone ever told you you look like Colette?"

It was something that all three of them had been saying to one another ever since Mademoiselle Rémy had first come, that her resemblance to Colette was extraordinary — the same short figure, round face with sharp features, tousled short hair and cat's eyes — and Rose's question (perhaps she'd been given the courage to ask it by the blackout) clearly delighted the nurse. "Oh, so often, Madame!" she cried, softly. "So many people remark on it. The extraordinary thing is, it isn't only in physical resemblance that Colette and I . . . You don't know, Madame, about Colette and me?"

Mrs. Curtius heard herself, not Rose, whisper "No" in the dark, and then — was it immediately? — things changed again. There was the sound of a door opening, a glow in the salon, and a cheerful voice announcing: *"Panne d'électricité!* Power failure throughout the hotel! But I couldn't leave my good friends in the dark! Here we are! *Soirée à la chandelle!*"

It was, of course, Madame Pierre, the trim, dynamic housekeeper, superhumanly efficient and yet with time and heart enough to have shown Mrs. Curtius the most extraordinary series of kindnesses during the past fortnight; indeed between the two ladies an esteem, even an affection, had sprung up and flourished, and it was Madame Pierre's constant dropping attentively in that had allowed Mrs. Curtius to spend her days without a day nurse or attendant, thank heaven, resting comfortably alone while her children, at her insistence, reexplored Paris — "retracing old footsteps for her," as dear Tom had growlingly put it.

"*Soirée à la chandelle!* They give them at Versailles for visitors of state — splendid gala evenings with the whole Galerie des Glaces lit by candles: why shouldn't we have one of our own?" The salon grew brighter, Mrs. Curtius could see Madame Pierre's figure darting about, placing candlesticks with lighted candles on the mantelpiece, on the commode, on the round table. The housekeeper must have arrived laden with several pairs of them. Mrs. Curtius could even make out the form and gleam of the two on the mantel — twisted gilt rococo imitation Louis XV, pretty and elegant in their way, typical of this hotel, an unspoiled monument to the Beaux-Arts' eighteenth-century revival of the year 1900. Suddenly the trim figure bearing a lighted candle appeared in her doorway and advanced toward her: there was a murmur of warning or protest from the salon; but Madame Pierre called back cheerfully, in her normal voice, "Oh, Madame is always glad to see me; we understand one another; I love Madame, and Madame loves me," and said it in the self-confident, optimistic way she had that was endearing, that no one could ever object to. She was a handsome, rather gaunt-faced woman; the candle, held before her, made her look like a figure from a painting by de la Tour; she came over, placed the candle expertly, somewhere in the background where the flame was no disturbance, approached the bed, bent down and kissed Mrs. Curtius on the forehead. "A candle for you to go to sleep by, my dear," she said. "Good night. Sweet dreams."

Mrs. Curtius held up a finger. "Tell them not to whisper," she said — she seemed to find it hard to speak much above a whisper herself — "I like to hear them."

"I'll tell them," the housekeeper promised, and went out.

Did she tell them? Mrs. Curtius did not know — after the arrival of the candle, perhaps she had dozed off for a moment. Perhaps for much longer. Perhaps Mademoiselle Rémy had tiptoed in to cast a glance at her a dozen times. It must still be not very late — the sky over the Faubourg St.-Germain wasn't yet quite black. She heard the pop of a champagne cork, the clear ring of a glass. "They *are* having a *soirée à la chandelle!*" she thought with delight, and, peering, she smiled to see the soft radiance of the room beyond.

"I can't tell you how strange it was, waiting for the Sultan to make up his mind," Madame Pierre was saying. "Supposedly, he *had* made up his mind — after all, his embassy here in Paris had engaged me, and I went out expecting to start work at once. But there was some palace intrigue. A certain official of the household wanted a different woman in residence, for reasons of his own. She was French, too, I believe. I think he was too obvious about it — that was why he couldn't manage it quickly, and why eventually, I was later told, he couldn't manage it at all. But the explanation given me while I waited was that the Sultan was delaying, reconsidering his decision to have a European woman housekeeper in the palace. It was such a break with tradition, might offend the wives, and so forth. My salary was paid faithfully. I lived in the town, in a hotel, expecting every day to be called to work. Eventually I got tired of waiting, and resigned, and came back to Paris and took this job where you see me now. The Sultan never received me. I only glimpsed him now and again as he went about the town on his business. I spent hours in the marketplace — unbelievably picturesque. Especially the tribesmen from the hills, with their robes and spears. Wild-looking, but with me so strangely and childishly gentle. Most of them spoke a little French, and we had conversations. Lots of laughing: they loved to joke. We exchanged addresses, and there is still a little correspondence. My room here in the hotel is on the top floor, rue de Bellechasse side. I have a lion skin on the floor that one of the warriors sent me a few New Years' ago. It was his evidence that he was a good provider — he wanted me to come out again, this time as his . . ."

Now the Left Bank sky was much darker.

Mrs. Curtius must have missed something: the voice was continuing, but it sounded different, like the voice of a man. "She longed so to see Paris again that we simply brought her. The doctor said we'd need luck if we were to get her home, and our luck's giving out fast."

"Sh, Tom . . . What was it, Mademoiselle Rémy, that you were going to tell us about Colette?"

"I have had many patients, Madame, many, many, both famous and obscure. There was none I loved more than Colette. Colette . . . I was her last nurse. Colette died in my arms, Madame."

There was a silence.

Suddenly, belatedly, Mrs. Curtius felt a stab of alarm. What was it they had been saying? Then the alarm quieted as she remembered that it was Colette they had been talking about, poor Colette, dying in Mademoiselle Rémy's arms. But why had Colette had to die? What had happened to her, exactly? For a moment Mrs. Curtius wanted to cry out, to demand loudly of the others, especially of Mademoiselle Rémy: "What happened? Tell me! What happened?" But even as she realized that in her weakness she couldn't ask anything loudly, she no longer wanted to ask at all, for she knew the answer. It had been given her by someone out there in the salon, a few minutes before. It was a remark about not having luck. Wasn't that what had been said, out there, about Colette? So different from her own case! This blessed luck of being able to be in Paris, to lie peacefully through a perfect Paris evening, watching the Paris sky go through its changes. How lucky she was!

The sky was very dark now, really black. But there was still a glow, a faint one, from the candles, and still a murmur, the lowest murmur, of voices from the salon. Tears came to Mrs. Curtius' eyes. How dear they all were, to bring her this joy! A *soirée à la chandelle* that went on and on, that was endless, or seemed to be. As endless as her marvelous luck . . . Mrs. Curtius felt the faintness coming over her again. She must remember to tell them that: how happy they had made her; how fortunate she felt herself to be.

(1965)

TRUE STORIES

Another Storyteller's Story

On her mother's side, my first wife Beatrice came of a storytelling family. Over the past century, several of its members were near-bards. Legends of the family itself never constituted more than a portion of their repertory; family and nonfamily material tended to be merged in a common reservoir of tales. Anecdotes concerning cousins and aunts were given all the dignity of legend, and the most exotic folk tales were apt to be recounted as though the events had happened a day or two before, just down the block.

The earliest member of the family to come to America was my wife's great-grandfather, who emigrated to this country from Germany in the 1840's — a refugee from the Judaic beliefs of his parents and forebears, which he did not share. His father and grandfather had been tutors of Greek and Latin to the children of the ruler of a small south German principality, and it had been supposed that he would follow in their footsteps. Instead, arriving in New York with some knowledge of English, he purchased a horse, a wagon, and a stock of household goods, and he traveled through the New England states peddling his wares. He chose that area because he had been told that the English spoken there was America's best. Later, he became a drygoods merchant in New York, and was associated with Felix Adler in the founding of the Ethical Culture Society.

In the garden of his house on Orchard Street grew a large pear tree, famous for the abundance of its fruit, much of which he distributed among his neighbors. He supposed that the tree had once been part of the orchard for which the street was named — a supposition that, over the years, gradually transformed itself, among his descendants, into the firmest kind of fact. On summer nights, under the Orchard Street pear tree, it was his custom to tell stories that he had heard as a boy in Germany to audiences composed of young people of the neighborhood. During the years of the Civil War, quite a number of adults — older men, and women whose husbands or sons were absent — swelled these groups of summer-night listeners. He brought such storytelling sessions to an end by rising and saying to his wife, "Let's go in, my dear. These people want to go home."

He always pruned the pear tree himself, on a certain day in September. In 1898, when he was eighty-four, he pruned the tree as usual. The day was unseasonably warm, he became overheated and then caught cold, pneumonia set in, and he died early in October. I have never heard any of his descendants, in recounting the story of his death, suggest that old age had anything to do with it.

His youngest, and only unmarried, daughter — one of Bea's great-aunts — was born in 1866. The previous year, her mother had had a miscarriage. "Younger members of the family have informed me," this great-aunt used to say, rather primly, to several generations of children, "that it is impossible to have a miscarriage for psychological reasons. So the story I always heard — that my mother had her accident as the result of her grief at hearing of Mr. Lincoln's death — cannot be strictly true. It happened the same day, however, and I know that she was deeply affected by the news. I imagine that on learning it she must have staggered and fallen, with the fatal outcome. Perhaps she even fell downstairs. In any case, I was conceived shortly thereafter."

Two of the great-aunt's sisters, one of them Bea's grandmother, were married, while still in their teens, to two young men who were friends and business partners, and who, like their new Orchard Street father-in-law, had immigrated from Germany and had become drygoods merchants. These younger men had gone not to New England but to Texas. There, in San Antonio, their venture had succeeded, and they had come to New York in search of wives. Within a year after the double wedding and the long bridal journey south — by train to St. Louis, the rest of the way by stagecoach — one of the sisters found the San Antonio heat unbearable, and persuaded her husband to move to New York. The other — Bea's grandmother — and her husband stayed on in Texas. She also suffered greatly from the heat, and often spent the hottest hours of the day in the comparatively cool cellar of her house. Her cook's husband, pastor of a San Antonio Negro church, discovered that she was literarily gifted, and he persuaded her to devote part of her cellar solitude each week to the composition of a sermon, which he would deliver the following Sunday. She had always possessed a naturally flowery style, both spoken and epistolary, and, thanks to the pastor's requirements, it lost none of its flamboyancy in Texas.

After several years, she, too, wearied of life in the South, and she and her husband followed the other couple to New York. Here they lived in a brownstone house at 12 East Eighty-first Street. The house still exists. It now has a brick façade, added by later owners. It was one of the first brownstones to be so "improved." When Bea's grandmother inhabited it, the ceilings of the parlor were painted with clouds and cherubs, and the gilt chairs and sofas below them were upholstered in "tapestry" depicting scenes from *Lohengrin*. Unlike many of her contemporaries, she did not consider such rooms out of bounds for children; children were even welcome to open the doors of the curio cabinet and finger, there, a set of miniature gold-filigree furniture, which included a sedan chair complete with lady passenger. And it was amid these elegant surroundings that the children of the family listened to her storytelling specialty, the folk tales of the brothers Grimm. Occasionally, Bea and I would meet, out at dinner in somebody's house, an elderly lady or gentleman who recalled with shudders her bloodcurdling rendering of "The Wolf and the Seven Little Kids."

One autumn, Bea's grandmother returned with her family from a year in Europe (bringing with her a dozen or more dresses by Worth and other Parisian couturiers) to find that the house, which everyone had supposed vacant during their absence, had been occupied, at least throughout the summer months. All the linen, all the silver, and all the lace — she loved lace and used it in cascades wherever possible — were gone. On the ceiling-high mirror in the front hall was written, in candle wax, "Thank you for your perfect taste and your summer's hospitality." Regrettably, someone had allowed the burglary insurance to lapse. In addition to the Grimm's tales and a florid English style, Bea's grandmother had at her command an endless stock of German proverbs. When the extent of the uninsured loss was revealed to her, she dryly and debonairly quoted a proverb that no one had heard before — one that, translated, ran, "From each according to his means; to each according to his needs." Her family — and, indeed, she herself — were quite surprised when someone discovered that it came from the works of Karl Marx; she was unable to say where she had acquired it.

When her husband, Bea's grandfather, was seventy, his sons and sons-in-law clubbed together and gave him a black buggy with yellow wheels. Thereafter, his grandchildren had many a delightful Sunday-morning drive with him along the Harlem

River Speedway. His coachman, who on weekdays drove him to his office and back in a sober closed carriage, sat on the buggy's small rear seat, his arms folded, as they skimmed along, the old gentleman holding the reins. As they went, he told stories about his early days in San Antonio — tales of cowboys and holdups, and of bears crashing into his garden in the middle of the night. His grandchildren thought of him almost as a hero of the Alamo, though I believe that at no time, even when his listeners were their youngest, did he conceal the fact that, while a Texan, he had been in the drygoods business.

Beatrice's mother, as a young girl, enjoyed two things particularly: visiting her favorite cousins at their country house in Mount Morris Park, and listening to her mother's storytelling. At an early age, she resolved to perfect herself in German. She had heard her grandparents converse now and then in that language, but in her own home it was employed only by her mother, when uttering proverbs. So Bea's mother studied German at Miss Brackett's school, and when she was sixteen she set herself a rule; she was a passionate lover of English novels, but she vowed never to read one without reading a book in German next. This rule she adhered to for several years. By the time of her marriage, she had acquired an enormous repertory of German, and other, tales. She and her husband bought a brownstone house at 63 East Eighty-fourth Street, and there she told these stories to her children, while her mother continued to tell the Grimm's stories on East Eighty-first Street. Perhaps because her mother had always overused German proverbs, this was the one form of literary expression that was anathema to my mother-in-law. "These people have a different smug saying for every conceivable contingency in life," she used to remark with annoyance. Occasionally, she would utter one herself, always with an air of wry amusement at its pompous patness.

Beatrice (later one of the habitués of her grandmother's story parlor, and one of the Sunday-morning passenger-listeners in her grandfather's buggy) was born in the house at 63 East Eighty-fourth Street, between Park and Madison Avenues. Neither the house nor its address now exists. The Regis High School spreads over the site. Bea and her brothers and their friends felt no hesitation about playing in the block, even though it was not then specifically marked, as it is today, "Play Street."

While Bea and her brothers were still small, their parents moved from East Eighty-fourth Street to 37 West Ninetieth Street, off Central Park West. (This house, too, has disappeared, and its address along with it. An apartment house is on the site.) The move was considered adventuresome. There were solid rows of houses on Ninetieth Street as far west as Columbus Avenue, but beyond that there were gaps. The rocky lot at the northeast corner of Amsterdam, with its wooden shack and its grazing goats, represented a way of living, Bea and her brothers felt, superior to their own. Their own took for granted the services of three seventeen-dollar-a-month Irish maids, whose normal rising hour was 5:30 A.M. Clara, the laundress, washed not only the linen but the windows. For Sunday-night supper, Bea was sometimes sent out to buy fresh rolls and pickles at Enoch's Delicatessen, on Columbus Avenue. In warm weather, she always bent down for a quick look under the swinging doors of the saloon at the southwest corner of Columbus and Ninetieth. She regretted that she was never sent there to have the household beer can refilled; that errand was always entrusted to one of the maids. "Farther west was largely Irish," Bea told me about Ninetieth Street beyond Columbus. "Half the children who came to the door on Halloween, asking for pennies, spoke with a brogue. Of course, they were all dressed up in tatterdemalion finery. Some of the costumes showed a lot of imagination." The maids, who had a downstairs sitting room, entertained their friends — and often the children of the house — by playing on a phonograph with a horn like a huge morning glory the records of Irish jigs and ballads they had brought from Ireland. Sometimes they supplemented these with tales of their own.

Not very surprisingly, perhaps, when Bea went to normal school, she specialized in storytelling. On her graduation, she was employed by welfare organizations to tell stories in settlement houses — chiefly to groups of children then known as court cases. These were neighborhood youngsters who had been, or whose parents had been, in difficulty with the law. Now and then, she was asked to tell stories in a hospital. Some of the children's wards included defective children, in those days, and for that reason were kept locked. The nurse in charge would lock Bea in, and come back for her at the end of the session. Sometimes there were a few sick prostitutes locked in, too — "because," as a nurse once said, "they have to be locked in someplace."

Once, on an afternoon shortly before Christmas, when Bea arrived at one of the settlement houses to give a special program of Yule tales, she found her audience larger than usual, augmented by a number of uninvited teen-age youths whom she had never before seen. Quite a few of these, she noticed, were carrying knives. Before beginning her first story, she announced that all knives were to be placed, for the duration of the program, on the table at which she sat. The adolescents courteously complied, and then listened to the tales with a demeanor no less rapt and respectful than that of the others. When the program was over, Bea induced them to stay on for one more story, "just for themselves." This, she felt, gave her regulars a fair chance of reaching home unscathed.

When I first knew Bea, she had already changed her profession, but occasionally I heard and saw her tell stories impromptu to youthful groups, usually composed of her nieces and nephews and their friends. The rapidity with which the children invariably fell under the spell of legend and folklore struck me as uncanny. The moment she began, there would be an instant, utter hush, and the sight of all the young faces staring intently at the storyteller always touched me — it was such a tribute to some eternal aspect of the telling of tales.

Some years ago, not having told stories except informally for a considerable time, Bea was invited to participate as a storyteller in a "preventive antidelinquency campaign" at a community center. The young supervisors in charge withdrew the invitation after two or three sessions, however. They were sorry, they said, but today's New York children needed more sophisticated fare than "The Daughter Who Was Born a Frog" from West Africa or "The One Who Loved Him Most" from the American plains. These stories "lacked relevance and didn't release enough tension," they said. Bea regretted this decision, especially since the community center children, apparently unaware of the inadequacy of the tales, had been listening to them with the same absorption shown by the settlement house children a generation before.

It was strange how, even when Bea was no longer a professional storyteller, the stories she used to tell kept cropping up, bringing responses from all kinds of people. It usually happened quite unexpectedly. There was an impromptu storytelling session one Halloween, in our apartment; we lived in a great big place, with hundreds of other families, on the East Side, not far from where Bea was born. Our doorbell hadn't rung during dinner that evening, and we were beginning to think there would be no children's visits for "trick or treat"; if so, it would be the first Halloween without them in all our years in New York. Then, just as we were leaving the table, there was a peal. A group of four children was at the door. Despite their various disguises — bought costumes, they were, every one of them — I had no difficulty in recognizing the children as junior co-tenants whom I had often glimpsed in lobby and elevator. They trooped into our foyer, and we handed out the nickels that they certainly didn't need, and then apples. When the apples appeared, one diminutive female spook lamented, "My pockets are so full of apples already I'm afraid I haven't room for this one."

"Would you like a story instead?" Bea asked.

Instantly the spook put her apple down on a table, and she and the others arranged themselves on the parquet floor, their masked faces upturned. The well-known hush fell. My wife chose a very brief tale; she knew they had other calls to make. She told them "The Monkey and the Jellyfish." When she had finished, there was a pause. The pause grew longer. Then one of the other masked listeners — this one in buckskin and feathers — reached up and tentatively laid his apple, too, on the table. Bea then told "The Traveling Musicians." After that, two more apples were placed confidently on the table, and two more short tales were told. "I guess that's that," Bea said then. "Everybody will be wondering where you are." The visitors wordlessly got to their feet, and only when they had filed out through the front door, which I had opened for them, did they burst into shrill thank-yous. Their voices streamed behind them as they disappeared toward the elevator.

Once Bea and I went to a cocktail party where we met a handsome, black-haired young man, introduced by our host as being from Oklahoma. "Are you a Chippewa?" Bea asked him, sociably. He nodded. "Then you must know my favorite Indian forest story," she said. " 'The Man Who Married the Moon.' "

"Not by that title, but tell it to me, and I'll tell you if it's one of ours," he said.

It was. Bea faltered a few times in the telling, being rusty, but the young man put her right each time. It was a curiously primeval antiphony to listen to, up there, high above Park Avenue. They finished in triumphant unison: "Then he found the girl whose face he had watched so many nights in the moon, and *he never came back to earth*." Quite a few of the other cocktail guests had gathered round to listen, and they seemed to find that ending entirely satisfactory.

At another party — a dinner, this time — there was a young woman who said proudly that her father had been a mighty teller of Irish tales. When Bea said that she, too, had told Irish stories, the young woman looked at her with mistrust. "Did

you tell 'The Bee, the Harp, the Mouse, and the Bum-clock'?"
she demanded.

"I did," Bea said.

"Well, when you got to the part about the pans and the
pails, what did you do with your hands?"

"I did this with them," said Bea, making a crisscross gesture.

"Bless you!" said the young woman. "There are those who
always do this" — she made a different gesture — "and that's
dead wrong, as you well know."

And then, one morning, one of the handymen of our apartment house came to make some repairs, and told Bea apologetically that some of the things she wanted him to do were
impossible. "Too bad you're not a Buddhist with an elephant,"
she said to him wistfully. "Everything is possible to a Buddhist if his elephant's the right one. Do you know the story
called 'The Well-Trained Elephant'? It was white, and it could
do all kinds of things, even when it was standing on one leg."

"I don't know the story, but I am a follower of yoga," the
man replied with dignity. "I stand on my head every morning."

"I've never seen that done the yoga way," Bea said. "Would
it be disrespectful if I asked you to show it to me?"

"Not at all," said the handyman, "if you don't tell the
superintendent."

Bea asked his permission to call in the maid, who she knew
would be interested, and, before the two ladies, the handyman
placed his hands and forearms on the floor, unfolded upward
gracefully and slowly, and was soon standing on his head,
chatting amiably about the diet he followed and about what a
shame it was that his wife was of too impatient a nature to
learn the yoga positions that he found so beneficial.

"He stayed there on his head at least five minutes," Bea
told me admiringly when I came home that night. "He
seemed utterly relaxed. He didn't even get red in the face.
Then he did all kinds of things for me around the house. Extra
things — things I'm sure he'd never have done if he hadn't
first stood on his head. Not as many as if he'd had the Well-

Trained Elephant to help him, naturally. He couldn't hope to
— I told him this in consolation, when he looked unhappy at
not being able to fix the faucet perfectly — because in the
story, of course, the elephant turns out to be Buddha himself."

(1958)

Jacques Villon: An Appreciation

Written as the introduction to the catalogue of an exhibition of Jacques Villon's etchings at the Seiferheld Gallery, New York, in 1964.

Almost everybody knows about the Duchamp family of six children, four of them artists, sons and daughters of the quiet, respectable notary, Eusèbe Duchamp, of Blainville, a Norman village not far from Rouen. One has often read how the oldest of the children, Gaston Duchamp, born in 1875 in Damville, changed his name to Jacques Villon when he abandoned the legal studies his father had urged him to pursue; how the next boy, Raymond, left medicine for sculpture, and out of dual loyalty to father and brother took the name Duchamp-Villon; how the father threw up his hands when the third son, Marcel, became an artist in turn; and how this paternal bowing to the inevitable made it unnecessary and inappropriate for Marcel, or Suzanne — the only artist among the three daughters — to use any name other than those they were born and christened with. (When Suzanne married the Swiss artist Jean Crotti she added his name to hers.)

What makes the story touching and singular is the mutual affection and comprehension that accompanied the children's having their own way. Monsieur Duchamp was no Dr. Flaubert, who was never known to open any book except medical books and unforgivably fell asleep when his son Gustave bravely began to read to him one of his youthful compositions as a plea to be allowed to follow a career of his own choosing. Monsieur Duchamp did his best to establish his sons in the solid professions, but he was no stranger to artistic activity. His wife was a talented draftswoman, and her father, Emile Nicolle, a retired ship broker in Rouen, was an etcher, usually busy on a plate representing one of the ancient buildings of the city. When Jacques Villon, then still Gaston Duchamp, left Blainville to become a boarder at the Rouen lycée, his local guardian was this elderly artist. Villon as I knew him was not a man for possessions, but among the few family treasures he always displayed with pleasure was an album of Emile Nicolle's Rouen etchings. "While I was at the lycée," he told me, "I had no time for art except on Sunday, when I went to my grandfather's." His first etching, made at sixteen, was a portrait of his grandfather, and his second, one of his father. His first lithographs were done on a press used by his father in his capacity as rural notary to multigraph (as we should call it) posters advertising sales of furniture or real estate or tracts of standing timber in Norman woods.

Indeed, Monsieur Duchamp's failure to make his elder son a lawyer was due in some part to the intervention of a person in his own camp. "One day, after I had worked as a notary's clerk for three months," Villon has said, "I accompanied my father to an estate sale of house-furnishings. An elderly notary who had been my father's predecessor was with us. He made it very clear that he regretted the career he had chosen for himself — it had, he said, given him '*une vie sans intérêt*,' and in my father's presence he encouraged me to follow my own bent."

"I never want there to be any real quarrels between any of you," Monsieur Duchamp had a stern way of saying when squabbles or resentments arose among the children. Scenes of family life and the house at Blainville are among the subjects of Gaston's and Marcel's paintings (an oil portrait of Monsieur Duchamp by Villon is in the Guggenheim Museum in New York, and he is the subject of the drypoint *Monsieur D. lisant*). In the last months of Jacques Villon's life I listened, in his studio at Puteaux, to three of the Duchamp children as they recalled with a mixture of pride and laughter how the respect felt by the villagers of Blainville for their father took the form, each July 14, of an evening visit to the notary's house by the local firemen's band — a visit always prepared for by the lighting of flares by the children and ample provision of Calvados by their parents.

When Gaston left the Rouen lycée to go to Paris in 1894, his father gave him an allowance of 150 francs a month on his promise to *"fréquenter"* the law school — that is, to register there and give it a try — but it was understood on both sides that for the young man the main attraction of the capital lay in its art world.

As to the change of name from Gaston Duchamp to Jacques Villon . . .

"The name Duchamp sounded too square for the glamorous new life Gaston was moving into," Marcel Duchamp has said. The "Villon" came from what Villon described to Dora Vallier as *"une incontestable parenté spirituelle"* between himself and the poet François Villon. "I felt that he and I had in common *l'amour pour une vie chaude, aimée pour elle-même,"* he once said to me, *"évitant les conventions sociales, vie insouciante."* Out of delicacy, he always pronounced the name giving the two *l*'s a pure *l* sound, and not the French *y* sound customarily used in pronouncing the name of the poet: "It seemed more respectful not to take over his name entirely," I once heard him say. (It might be noted here that Villon wasn't the poet's real name either: Sainte-Beuve tells us that he was born François Corbeuil and took the name Villon from his "*maître*.")

The "Jacques" he took because of a "*grande sympathie*" for Daudet's novel, *Jack*. Indeed he spelled it "Jack" at first, and the name "Jack Villon" was signed to a few very early drawings that were never published. Does anyone read *Jack* nowadays? When it appeared in 1876, Henry James was in Paris, and he lamented the narrow vision of his French literary acquaintances, none of whom had heard of George Eliot's *Daniel Deronda* although they were all (James says belittlingly) reading *Jack*. Today *Jack* seems a masterpiece of sentimentality. And yet one can understand that Gaston Duchamp, reading it as a young man, should have had a "*grande sympathie*" for this story of a sensitive boy broken by the harshness and brutality of an industrialized, workaday world. I can remember Villon, in one of his later years, speaking of an acquaintance whose steady refusal to soil his hands with work of any kind was notorious, and who was commonly referred to by those who knew him as a parasite. "I can't help feeling a certain admiration for him," Villon said. "At least he has succeeded in keeping himself outside the rat race of the age we live in." In the novel, Jack's great persecutor, his mother's lover, constantly preaches to the boy on the theme "*Ce siècle est un siècle de fer*," and "*La vie n'est pas un roman*," in the sense of "Life is no romantic dream"; and there exists a sketch by Villon dated 1900 showing only a beautifully drawn baby carriage with a baby in it, over the caption: "*La vie n'est pas un roman* — Alphonse Daudet, 'Jack'." And, with further reference to this novel that was obviously so important to Villon, anyone who reads it in the familiar Flammarion edition with illustrations by Myrbach is in for something of a surprise if he compares Myrbach's drawing, on page 330, of the ironworks where poor Jack leads his brutifying existence, with Villon's Cubist painting (not the etching) of 1914 entitled *L'Atelier de Mécanique*, at present in a private collection in New York.

Soon the self-christened young artist was living in Montmartre, studying briefly with the academic painter Fernand Cormon, making humorous drawings for weekly newspapers as Juan Gris was doing at the same time, using as his models passersby in the streets or hiring them in the outdoor "models market" around the fountain in the Place Pigalle, enjoying his artist's pass that allowed him free entry into the Moulin Rouge, where he could watch Toulouse-Lautrec ("it was he who had the greatest influence on us all; I went to his studio only once, with Francis Jourdain") entertaining friends and drawing as they drank. Then he began to make aquatints printed in color; and then, his interest in the possibilities of painting stimulated by the first Cubists, he deepened his concepts of art. In 1906 he and his beautiful young Gaby moved from Montmartre to the quiet studio in Puteaux where he lived the rest of his life; and he founded the group called the "*Section d'Or*," with his brothers, La Fresnaye, Picabia, Gleizes, Metzinger, Delaunay, Apollinaire, and others meeting to discuss paintings and theory at Puteaux and at nearby Courbevoie in the studio of Gleizes. After the First World War came the series of interpretations in color aquatint of the works of other modern artists; and, from 1930, uninterrupted painting, with recognition and financial ease coming only after another World War had begun.

Such is the familiar outline of Jacques Villon's career, an outline found in the opening pages of the catalogues of many of his exhibitions. It can be expanded a little, in words that are Villon's own.

One day in 1954, when Villon was seventy-nine, he told me that there were a few things that he would like to say about episodes in his life. I took my typewriter to Puteaux, and Villon dictated fragments of autobiography, using the third person. One copy of the little essay was sent to Lionello Venturi, who was about to write his book on Villon (published only in 1962), and Villon apparently referred to it also in cooperating with Dora Vallier for her excellent *Jacques Villon, Oeuvres de 1897 à 1956* (Paris, Editions "Cahiers d'Art," 1956). But the pages themselves, as they were tapped out that afternoon in the studio, may give something of the flavor of the Jacques Villon who retained all the gentleness and the firmness of the Gaston Duchamp who had had his own way sixty years before. Here, put into English, are portions of those pages as Villon dictated them and then corrected them:

Between 1894 and 1910, JV made drawings for weekly newspapers, chiefly for *Le Courrier Français,* an interesting paper that employed a few artists — Forain, Willette, Louis Legrand, Lautrec, etc. Up to a certain point, JV still thinks that this work was not without its usefulness, for it is a kind of work that offers many opportunities both to observe life as it passes by and to gain insight into people's mentalities. However, if JV were to live his life over, he would not make drawings for newspapers. He was led to do so by a certain pride: his father had wanted him to study law, and he was living in the rue des Ecoles (with his brother Duchamp-Villon, who was studying medicine at the time), receiving 150 francs a month from his father. But this situation did not completely satisfy JV (who was still called Gaston Duchamp); he was afraid of being too much of a burden to his father, for there were four other children still living at home. He began to draw for newspapers because in addition to promising quick financial independence it seemed sufficiently compatible with his own artistic interests. But drawing for newspapers is a little like Nessus's shirt — it isn't easy to get free from it; JV took it up without attaching too much importance to it, but it went on for fifteen years. He realized that newspaper work alone was a dead end, and after 1899, following his return from his military service, he divided his time between the newspapers and etching.

JV's print-making, thus begun as a continuous activity in 1899 and interrupted only by the war, 1914–1919, will probably not stop until . . . it has to. About 1899 he also made several posters. At that time there was a very lively revival of interest in color aquatints. JV was then living in Montmartre, in the rue Caulaincourt, and it was his neighbor, Francis Jourdain, who initiated him into the secrets of that special technique, as exemplified in the eighteenth-century color aquatints by Debucourt, Janinet, etc., then in such great demand. His color aquatints were published by Edmond Sagot, with whom he was to preserve a steady relationship until the appearance of Cubism. About 1912 JV made a series of Cubist plates — a development that was hard for Sagot to follow. Sagot and Villon had a very friendly discussion and Sagot advised JV to see his brother, Clovis Sagot, who was at that time close to Picasso and the avant-garde movement, and to ask him to publish his new work. He did just that. (JV was already acquainted with Clovis Sagot, having seen him come more than once to ask his brother Edmond's help in financing his purchase of the works of various artists. The two brothers were on excellent terms, although they looked at art with different eyes. Edmond had a very prosperous business, whereas Clovis was in continual financial straits.)

Although devoting himself chiefly to the newspapers and to etching, Villon did not completely neglect painting. Not that it particularly attracted him. When his friends went off to make a sketch from nature along the banks of the Seine before drinking an apéritif, he felt no need to accompany them. It was almost as though he sensed that painting was about to take a new turn and that such little country sketches had no particular point. However, he exhibited both paintings and etchings at the Salon de la Nationale and at the Salon d'Automne.

Only around 1907–1908 did he begin to devote more of his time to painting. (His rare pictures of around 1900 had apparently been influenced by Manet, by Degas.) Now there was a tendency to analyze volumes and to use brighter colors. Toward 1908 the color became more "fauve," and in 1911, at the moment of the Cubist exhibition, JV felt that he was definitely a painter. In Cubism he found a method that enabled the painter to abandon the "open window" of the Impressionists: this broadened his scope and made him a true creator. Nevertheless, JV never repudiated color, unlike other Cubists who used earth tones and blacks; as a result, JV was called *"le cubiste impressioniste."*

JV's fifteen years of drawing for newspapers could have been wasted years — but in fact they were not. The need to observe life and catch it on the wing gave his art a special graphism that might be related to Bergson's "line of intention." This line becomes the vertebral column of the picture, the tightrope that determines the distribution of values. This is exemplified in *La Table Servie*, a canvas of 1912, exhibited in the Salon d'Automne.

The war of 1914–1918 gave JV plenty of time to ponder his art in the trenches. Demobilized and back in his Puteaux studio, he felt the need to push his investigations further, and he took up abstract painting as a means of producing autonomous creations. But with him a painting was never an arbitrary creation: he always felt impelled to start from observation of nature, a nature perhaps enhanced by intuition, and his work has oscillated between complete abstraction and an abstraction that is more human.

By 1920 pressing financial need obliged JV to turn once again to etching. It was then that he made about forty color aquatints, of rather large format, after paintings by his fellow artists, Picasso, Matisse, etc. At this time he also etched plates for a book on architecture.

Because of all these types of work — newspaper drawings, color aquatints, reproductions — JV unquestionably found himself, as a painter, twenty-five to thirty years behind his fellow artists. Some of the latter still tend to look upon him, somewhat dogmatically, as a print-maker, and even as a *"graveur-ouvrier"* — a fact that he had never fully appreciated until very recently. Apparently one must live a long time before one can assert oneself fully! But let us not feel sorry for JV: all has turned out for the best, and his prints live in happy intelligence with his paintings.

Most of JV's newspaper drawings were published in *Le Courrier Français*, between 1897 and 1911. For his color aquatints from 1899 to 1913 he had only one publisher: Edmond Sagot. For his interpretations in color aquatint after the war, also only one publisher: his brother-in-law, the painter Jean Crotti. Throughout those years, indeed up until 1942, JV had no dealer who handled his paintings. He had never submitted a painting to a dealer, even though by 1930 he felt himself completely liberated from his past as an etcher and was in a position, from that time on, to devote himself exclusively to painting. Why he never submitted a painting to a dealer is a question he often asks himself. During those years he contented himself with the salons — Salon d'Automne (he was on the Committee from 1904 to 1912), Salon des Tuileries, Salon des Indépendants — and with occasional one-man exhibitions. This state of affairs certainly did nothing to help the sale and circulation of works by Villon. However, it must be said that about 1934 young painters began to display an interest in his work, an interest that continues today. (In 1913, on the occasion of the Armory Show in New York, American collectors became interested in his work, and have always remained so.) To complete the list of JV's few but faithful dealers and publishers we should add, in respect to his paintings, the name of the Galerie Louis Carré, to which he has belonged since 1942.

It was just about 1930, the year Villon marks as the beginning of his "liberation from his past as an etcher" and of his ability to devote himself entirely to painting, that I was first taken to his studio by his pupil, Beatrice Stein, the "Miss Bea" of his etching, an American who had been introduced to him by her first teacher, Walter Pach. Pach had met Villon and his brothers in 1913 while in Paris gathering pictures for the Armory Show, and much of the early interest manifested for Villon in America (as evidenced by the presence of Villon paintings and etchings in collections in Chicago, Columbus, New York, and elsewhere) was generated by Pach: indeed my very first visit to the studio that day in such company was a small portion of that interest. My admiration for him as an artist soon came to be equaled by my regard for him as a man.

Here was a recognized master print-maker who was a devoted and determined painter; who, freely acknowledging his stimulation by the earliest Cubists, had pushed beyond facile sketches to produce, in *La Table Servie* of 1912 and other paintings done shortly before the war, some of the most beautiful paintings of Cubism, and who, after having had "plenty of time to ponder his art in the trenches . . . felt the need to push his investigations further." But along with that obligation he felt another — an obligation that recalls the "pride" and desire for independence that made him take up newspaper drawing in the first place — the duty to support himself and his wife; and at the price of being set further "behind his fellow artists" in his development as a painter he did not hesitate to turn to his etching skill to reproduce the paintings of others in order to meet material requirements — modest enough, as anyone who ever visited the Puteaux house and studio will testify. "A man who practices as a trade something he had begun as an occupation is justified by the need to earn his bread," Villon once said to me about this period. "There is no reason to be either proud or ashamed of it: the important thing is to continue it no longer than necessary."

By the time I met Villon he was painting again — "liberated" (he meant, of course, not from all etching, but from the need to make reproductive color aquatints for a livelihood) — and one could see and sense the experimentation, the "investigations" into color and light, of which each new canvas was the result. One could see also something else — the racks of finished canvases, dozens of them, dating well back before Cubism, that were stacked there in the studio, unsold. *La Table Servie* was among them, until Beatrice Stein bought it; *Instruments de Musique* (on wooden panels; now in the Art Institute of Chicago) was there until she and I bought it soon after our marriage; and many another, including the beautiful *Soldats en marche*, remained there until 1942, when Louis Carré bought, with some exceptions, the contents of the studio and arranged to handle his future work. In the 1930's the studio also contained many a portfolio of unsold etchings, including some of the Cubist plates.

When Villon said in 1954 that some of his fellow artists continued to consider him as a print-maker and even as a "*graveur-ouvrier*," and that he had not fully realized that fact "until very recently," the limpidity of his character was keeping him, I think, from seeing that it may well not have been "until very recently" that such opinions had been expressed. Only "very recently" had Villon become, in painting, a "success" *: and fellow artists seldom take the trouble to make derogatory remarks about a colleague until he is a "success." The respect felt by his fellow artists for Villon, both as etcher

---

* Carnegie Prize (1950); retrospective exhibition at the Musée d'Art Moderne, Paris (1951); exhibitions at the Galerie Carré.

and as painter, was strongly apparent to anyone who knew artists in Paris in the 1930's. During the years when, in reproducing their pictures in color aquatints he was performing a comparatively humble task (if the word "humble" can be used in any connection with those beautiful plates), they considered him their colleague. Matisse was apparently the unique exception. *"Voulez-vous m'appeler Monsieur Matisse, s'il vous plaît,"* he requested one day when Villon addressed him by his last name alone, as the painters were accustomed to address each other. It was not until Villon had one of his first "successes" — an exhibition that was in some ways his most thrilling, the display of his recent paintings in 1945, after the liberation of Paris and V-E Day, at the Galerie Louis Carré — that Picasso, asked if he was going to attend the vernissage, said, "What? In this weather?"

That story was not told me by Villon, although he had heard it. His reminiscence of Matisse's haughtiness was his *only* unfavorable quotation of a colleague's remarks, his *only* unfavorable remark concerning another artist either personally or artistically, that I can recall over a period of more than thirty years. A few years ago, when I remarked that in my visits to Paris galleries I had not seen the work of any young painter that seemed to me interesting he replied defensively that, in general, the work of young painters in Paris was on a high level of competence, and that little of it was absurd: "Only the pictures sold on the street [he meant in open-air exhibitions like those around Washington Square or on Piccadilly] are absurd." Young painters constantly wrote him, telephoned him, or, after he secured an unlisted telephone number, arrived unannounced at the studio with armfuls of their work. It was a measure of Villon's fading vitality and spirits, not of any change in the Paris scene, that when I asked him, the very last time I saw him, in 1963: "Do you know of someone new whose work I should see?" tears came to his eyes and he shook his head.

Villon's refusal to speak ill of anyone came out amusingly when I read him what Yvette Guilbert wrote in her memoirs about Jules Roques, the editor of *Le Courrier Français*, the newspaper in which Villon's earliest drawings had chiefly appeared: "All the artists who drew for his newspaper complained about him. Roques paid them badly, they said, and he often kept their drawings, holding an exhibition and sale of them each year that brought him in a good deal of money. Willette left him, and even broke angrily with him." "*Exageré!*" Villon cried, when I read him that. "Perhaps even false! A coldness between Willette and Roques, perhaps, but nothing worse. It wasn't always hard to get your money from Roques. The thing to do was to take your drawings and be at his house, Avenue de Trudaine, on Monday morning at seven o'clock. There was always a cab waiting for him there at that time, to take him around to his various offices. The newspaper was only one of his interests — he was in all kinds of business, a champagne company and heaven knows what else. If he happened to have money on him he'd pay you on the spot for the drawing or drawings he accepted, and paid well. If not, it was bad luck — sometimes if you weren't paid for the week's drawing on Monday morning, payment was forgotten. But Roques was 'somebody.' After he died, in 1910, almost none of us were interested in drawing for the newspaper. I stopped two weeks after his death." I asked Villon whether his remark to Dora Vallier, reported in her book — "If I had been more wide-awake, drawing for newspapers would have been more rewarding" — meant that he felt that he had been naïve financially, that Roques had underpaid him. "I wasn't referring to money!" he protested. "What I meant was that I should have noted down many more things than I did as I walked about with my sketchbook." It was only after a little more conversation that it turned out that Yvette Guilbert may, perhaps, have been more right than wrong: "Well," Villon finally admitted, reluctantly, "of course we all should have been paid a little more than we were . . ."

Villon had no comment to make on Roques's annual exhibition and sale of artists' drawings that roused Yvette Guilbert's indignation on their behalf, but he had reason to remember another such exhibition, in the offices of another newspaper. "I had some sketches on exhibition in the newsroom of the *Chat Noir* in 1895 or 1896. The director told me that he had led a certain visitor around the room full of drawings and the visitor said that only mine were of any interest. The visitor was Degas. Of course such words, and the repetition of them to me by the director, were a message — an invitation to the young artist to call on the master. And certainly I should have called on Degas. He seldom left such messages. I admired Degas tremendously, of course. But I never called on him."

"Why not?"

"*Timidité.*"

Villon also spoke of his great admiration for Ingres. "Some of his work is disagreeable, but still . . . And what some people seem not to realize is that there are different *kinds* of drawing by Ingres." As to Manet: "You could *eat* his painting.* He loved to spread on paint, like Courbet. Today we tend to be less literal." One of his favorite modern artists was Klee. When I asked him whether he preferred him as draftsman or as painter: "He is equally good as both — great sensibility."

It is almost possible to excuse those of Villon's fellow artists who, after his "success" as a painter, preferred to continue to think of him as a print-maker, because a number of particularly fine and immediately acclaimed etchings and drypoints were produced in the 1930's, when he was painting pictures that did not bring him immediate success. Portraits, landscapes, human figures, still lifes — often the same subjects that were being depicted, or would later be depicted, on canvas: there were always new Villon etchings to be seen at the annual exhibitions of the Société des Peintres-Graveurs. In the spring of 1936 Villon spent a few weeks in the United States,

* An echo of Madame de Sévigné's expression of admiration for an essay of Nicole: "I'd like to make a broth of it and swallow it." Villon retained much from the excellent classical lycée education of his generation in France. Once we were playing a parlor game that consisted of filling out, for a variety of great men, the kind of questionnaire so often encountered in today's bureaucracies, and when we came to "Socrates. Occupation ———" Villon triumphed with Socrates' own self-characterization: "Midwife."

visiting Katherine Dreier (founder of the Société Anonyme) and Walter Pach, who was at that time teaching at Bowdoin College. He made his headquarters the apartment of Mrs. Gerda Stein at 300 Central Park West, from which he did his pair of lithographs of New York skylines. A few years later we were urging him to come again, this time with Madame Villon, to escape the holocaust, but I remember his answer: "*Il faut rester avec son tribu.*"

Odilon Redon once said that "Of all the states of mind propitious to artistic or intellectual creation, none is more fruitful than the grief produced by national disaster." Whether or not those words are valid, Villon did magnificent work during those years that were so bitter and so exalting for his "*tribu.*" The months of the "phony" war, spent at Beaugency on the Loire, brought drawings for two beautiful etchings, *Le Pont de Beaugency* and *Les Trois Ordres;* then, on a southern farm called La Brunié, in unoccupied France, came the beginning of a series of canvases of market gardens, their flat planes and tall windbreak backgrounds flooded with a light that was new in Villon's work. Back in Paris, the subjects of the two Beaugency etchings were used for paintings; and from then on there followed the "series of series" that looms large in Villon's last twenty years of painting — the self-portraits, the harvest series, the several airplane series, the baby series, the Norman dovecote series, the portraits of Marcel Duchamp, and lastly the Rouen dock-crane series that form a career's end as monumental as Monet's *Nymphéas.* It was a self-portrait painted in 1942 that caused the dealer Louis Carré to seek out Villon and agree to buy his entire production; and just as some critics will always value Villon's Cubist paintings more highly than all the rest, others consider his canvases of the 1940's his supreme accomplishment.

What seems to have occurred at this time was a breakthrough in Villon's experiments with color and light. "Why suggest light effects when color can be made to behave like light itself?" he said to Dora Vallier. "Color can be applied to the canvas as if it were light." It is a feature of many of Villon's canvases of the 1940's that, as Jerome Mellquist put it, they "catch fire." The color harmonies are incandescent, and seem actually to generate light. This gives these pictures a "smashing" quality that perhaps accounts for their particular popularity. A general *"élan,"* probably related to this new color brilliance, seized Villon at this time, and from now on many canvases were of larger sizes than formerly. Nevertheless, Villon always saw his own work as a continuum, and when asked "Do you consider that in general your paintings after 1940 are more 'important' than the preceding ones?" he answered simply "No."

He had always longed for the opportunity to decorate a large surface, and in the 1950's this desire was fulfilled in an exciting and gratifying way by a commission to execute a series of stained glass windows for the cathedral at Metz. This was the culmination of Villon's love of color and light. The strenuous physical effort involved — the climbing up and down ladders, the traveling back and forth between Paris and Metz — brought, in his late seventies, the first lament I heard from him about his age: "Oh to be younger and able to do many of these things!"

In 1956 he won the Grand Prix of the Venice Biennale, and on this occasion and on one or two subsequent ones he traveled to Italy, which he had never visited during his first eight decades. This painter, whom we have heard speak of his indebtedness first to Toulouse-Lautrec, then to Degas and Manet, and then to the first Cubists, and who revered Cézanne and Seurat, had never been a student of art history, accustomed though he was, as founder of the *"Section d'Or,"* to study the aesthetic theories of Alberti, Leonardo, and other early artists. Consequently his friends were sometimes amused by the tone of his immensely respectful comments on masterpieces so belatedly seen in Italy. *"Pas mal, ce Titien!" "Les Tintorets dans l'Ecole de Saint-Roque — c'est impressionnant, ça!"* He made the discoveries very much his own.

Although he had abandoned drawing for newspapers in 1910, Villon resumed illustrating, on a different plane, in the

1930's. His first gift to me was a copy of *En Flanant dans le Jardin du Livre Illustré*, by his friend Jean-Paul Dubray, the gentle poet and librarian who is the model in two great Villon etchings, *Le Poète* and *Le Savant*. Dubray's charming book, published *aux dépens de l'auteur* in Paris in 1936, tells of Villon's recent reemergence as an illustrator of various deluxe editions of classic and modern authors. Subsequently, the illustration of those special editions, beautifully printed on splendid paper, which are such a Parisian specialty, became one of Villon's recurrent activities. Notable are a lofty black and white *Cantique Spirituel*, of Racine, and above all, a *Bucoliques*, put into French by Paul Valéry, with colored lithographs that have become justly famous. Not least, though almost last, among them, is a delicious little *A poèmes rompus*, by Max Jacob, with abstract plates in color.

In 1955 as an afterword in Jacques Lassaigne's study, *Eloge de Jacques Villon*, Villon wrote a few pages on etching, which might be included here in what I think is their first translation into English:

> I love color; I thrive on paint.
> And yet it was not to color that I devoted my first years of apprenticeship, but to etching, to lithography, in short to prints, then to drawing.
> Why? My friend Jacques Lassaigne has just said it: because I had before me the example of my grandfather, an etcher. But also, and especially, because graphism, holding as it does the idea in a tight grasp — catching it in a lasso, so to speak — seemed most suited to the cast of my mind, which was fascinated by gestures and attitudes and eager to collect them. I collected them not as some pin butterflies to a board, but rather, conceiving each of them as something autonomous. I sought, as it were, to synthesize, to concretize a passing moment in order to render it eternal, to show it in a special, enduring light; and I did this through mysterious networks of lines on plates that were then made to confide their secrets to paper.
> Drawing is controlled by the emotion it releases, an emotion that corresponds to that which gives it birth. It can

stray, return to its path, and depart again: it is, above all, exploration.

Etching, on the other hand, might be said to control the artist: it demands the utmost precision. In order to master a difficult material, the etcher must (at least in his head) order everything in advance; he must look upon his plate as a canvas, and divide it harmoniously. Thus an etching is not merely a drawing executed more or less rapidly on a copper plate.

The draftsman turned etcher must renounce the subtlety peculiar to drawing — that subtlety that expresses itself in taking a thousand steps ahead, a thousand steps back, as though, guided by a thread, the artist has to find his way out of a labyrinth. In etching the subtleties of drawing are expressed in depth, so to speak. A tone, indicated by means of a certain number of parallel lines, hatchings, and crosshatchings, exposed to the acid, section by section for periods of between two and twenty-five minutes, displays a gamut of values that could be indicated in drawing merely by increasing the pressure of the pencil, or if ink is used, by multiplying the number of intersecting lines.

Although, in etching, drawing is simplified, the thousand refinements of the mind that direct the hand are nonetheless present. I speak, of course, of etchings by painters. To the contrast between the black of the ink and the white of the paper, the acid-bitten line adds a richness of its own: becoming absorbed in the paper, it produces an effect of blurring and shading.

Were Gulliver to enlarge a proof of one of our etchings, the lines would seem transformed into a fortified city, a work in relief, almost as though the paper were composed of several overlapping sheets. Could we retain such an illusion as that, our suspense might be all the greater as we watch the final print come off the handpress.

Here are some lines that Villon wrote in 1958 to a younger painter, once his pupil, who was thinking of having an exhibition of delicate paintings in Paris and asked him whether he would write an introduction to the catalogue:

Of course I will. How could I not do it? Why ever should I refuse?

I know with what faith, despite almost insurmountable difficulties, you have given all you have to painting, and how, without forcing, you have been able to produce a body of work that is a lasting and authentic expression of a sensitive mind, one undeceived by mere appearances — which are no more than the sign of something, but the sign of what? Is not the true treasure, after all, the plowed and turned field that yields heavy ears of wheat, rich with all the juices of the earth?

This field will not be the less valuable if it is a garden, and if a spade has been used rather than a tractor.

"An overwhelming proportion of the great prints have been made by painters rather than by professional etchers or lithographers," William S. Ivins once wrote.

With Jacques Villon there disappeared a painter *and* a professional print-maker, whose canvases are indeed like a panorama of fields, lit by special and enduring lights of the artist's own making, rich with crops indigenous to Normandy and southern France, and whose prints are like a not less valuable garden, a true treasure, filled with the thousand refinements of the mind that directed the artist's hand.

Postscript: Marcel Duchamp Fifty Years after the Nude

Nearly sixteen hundred works made up the International Exhibition of Modern Art which opened at New York's 69th Regiment Armory on February 17, 1913. One of the paintings became the public's symbol of everything that was scandalous, absurd, or morally outrageous about the revolutionary art on display at the Armory Show, as the exhibit came to be called. That painting was Nude Descending a Staircase, *a cascade of cubes by a twenty-five-year-old Frenchman, Marcel Duchamp.*

The show was partially reconstituted fifty years after, in February 1963, by the Munson-Williams-Proctor Institute, in Utica, New York, and then reinstalled for a few weeks in New York City in its old Armory home. Marcel Duchamp attended the vernissage as honored guest and later lectured visitors on modern art. He was living in Greenwich Village, where I interviewed him for Show *magazine.*

We might be in Paris, the ceilings in this old town house are so high, the rooms so big; and the Master himself . . .

"You are a Master, you know, Marcel; that's why I've been asked to interview you."

"If I'm a Master, you're a ————."

. . . the host himself, despite his plaid American sport shirt, can't escape looking Gallic enough to have been drawn by Clouet. There are two chess tables; on the walls hang canvases by Tanguy, Miró, Matisse, Picabia, Wifredo Lam; over the fireplace is a sheet of glass, a "sketch" for the big *Bride Stripped Bare by Her Bachelors, Even* in the Yale University Art Gallery; on the coffee table is one of the most artistic of the Duchamp artifacts, the *Coin de Chasteté* (*coin* in the sense of "wedge") — a hollow model of a certain female zone, with meticulously fitting (removable) metal inset.

"How old am I now? Same age as ever. Seventy-five, going on seventy-six to be exact. A mere child, as things go in our family. My brother Jacques Villon at eighty-seven is still painting splendidly; just the other day I saw a canvas on the easel in his studio in Puteaux, very vivid, very strong . . ."

"Is it true that he changed his name from Gaston Duchamp because your father was opposed to his giving up the law and becoming a painter?"

"Painting was romance to Gaston in 1900 — was then, still is, always will be. The name Duchamp sounded too square for the glamorous new life he was moving into. My brother Raymond did half and half, called himself Duchamp-Villon. He was the *Wunderkind*. His first sculpture was accepted by the Salon de la Nationale when he was a nineteen-year-old medical student. Sensation in the family! He gave up medicine until he used it in the war as a medical officer; and then, of course, he died."

"And you? Did you ever study for a profession?"

"Oh, when I was sixteen I thought for about six months that I'd like to be a notary like my father, but that was just because I loved my father. I *adored* my brothers. There was all this drawing and painting and sculpting going on around me by this time. Look at these old sketches of mine I found the other day, done when I was eighteen. *Exactly* like what Gaston was doing then. Fantastic!"

"Quite a distance between them and the *Nude Descending a Staircase*, done only eight years later. You never did see the Armory Show, did you, where it caused such a scandal?"

"How could I get to the Armory Show? In 1913 I was a librarian in the Bibliothèque Sainte-Geneviève, earning five francs a day. All I knew about the Armory Show was that Walter Pach wrote me that my three pictures had been sold . . ."

"Librarian? Why librarian?"

"Because I wanted a nice quiet job that would pay my room and board and let me do what I wanted with my leisure. I was through with the world of the artists, *through*."

"Through, at twenty-five?"

"Absolutely. When the Cubists themselves asked me to remove the *Nude Descending* from the Salon des Indépendants in February 1912 because they thought it would be considered a joke on Cubism, I said 'To hell with them,' and I wanted no more of them. I realized my aims were different from theirs. Take my brother again, Jacques Villon. One of the very best painters today. Steadily French, not corrupted by internationalism. Kaleidoscopic, not repeating and imitating himself like other painters, who stop being creators and turn into performers. Villon always had fame in one way or another — as cartoonist first, as etcher, among artists. Now he is *world* famous. If ever anybody deserved to be, it's he: he got there without ever compromising himself; no tricks. He loves it, and I love it for *him*. But back there in 1912 I realized how different I was even from my brother. He aimed at fame. I *had* no aim. I just wanted to be left alone to do what I liked."

"And when Walter Pach wrote you that the *Nude Descending* had been sold in New York . . ."

"The *Nude Descending*, the *King and Queen Surrounded*

by *Swift Nudes* and the *Chess Players*. I was very happy to have the money. I cleared about six hundred dollars for the three. Then in 1915 Pach persuaded me to try my luck in the States, and I came over . . ."

"No military service in the war?"

"Exempted. I was debilitated. In the States I gave French lessons at two dollars an hour. Very profitable and nice. Charming people invited you to dinner . . . I sold the few pictures I had to John Quinn and the Arensbergs. *They* asked me to dinner. Dinner at the Brevoort, a dollar twenty-five. Very good. Always a Bronx or Manhattan first. 'We had a Bronx last night. Let's have a Manhattan tonight.' Never anything else. Such a pleasant feeling in the States in those days. A real democracy, such a contrast from French feudalism. No union dictatorship, like today. More freedom for certain groups today, less for the individual. There was a real Bohemia. Delightful. Why, Greenwich Village was full of people doing absolutely *nothing!* Now they feel they have to take drugs, at least. Nineteen twenty-nine was the point of greatest scission, of course. The greatest change comes from taxes. People are completely different when they have to pay a lot of taxes. They *buy art* because of taxes! Talk about *lèse majesté* — what about *lèse* art? It means gifts to museums — there's that good side — but what do you see good going on in art except the acquisition of good, older pictures by museums?"

"Marcel, in 1915 you gave French lessons and sold the few pictures you had, and you've lived in the States more or less ever since — with long stays in France. What have you *done* since 1915?"

"Well, I've painted no pictures on canvas since 1918; the last one was called *Tu m'e* — that *e* can be considered the first letter of any verb you like. In the teens I did my 'ready-mades,' like the urinal I sent to the Independents in New York in 1917, and the 1919 *Air de Paris*, a flask I had filled with air in Paris and brought over here. I stopped doing my glass panels in 1923. For a while I did a little color research with revolving discs — there's one at Yale that I did with Man Ray;

it almost killed him, one of the discs flew off and hit him in the head; it was reproduced and exhibited in a show in Stockholm a year or so ago, called 'Motion in Art,' or something like that. Then I put together a lot of my sketches into two portfolios, one called the *Green Box* and the other the *Valise*. But I've really done nothing, you might say, since about 1923. Does a certain amount have to be done? You know how time passes. Wars come. Somehow one doesn't work. I'm not a man of decisions. I didn't *decide* to stop painting, or working with glass, or doing 'ready-mades.' Of course, I've always played some chess. But even that's different now. I used to want to be a chess champion. Now I just play chess."

"*Show* will want me to ask you this: if you've done nothing since 1923, what have you lived on?"

"Tell *Show* I'll answer that one when I get a complete financial dossier concerning every member of the staff of *Show*."

"You know you're one of the most famous artists in the world . . ."

"I know no such thing. For one thing, *les petites gens* — the grocers — don't know my name, the way most of them have heard of Dali and Picasso and even Matisse. For another thing, if one is famous, I think it must be impossible to know it. Being famous is like being dead: I don't suppose the dead know they're dead. And thirdly, if I *were* famous I couldn't be very proud of it: it would be a clownish sort of fame, dating back to the sensation caused by the *Nude Descending*. Though, of course, I suppose that if that kind of infamy lasts fifty years, then there's more to it than just the scandal."

"What else is there?"

"There's *It*."

"*It?*"

"*It*. Whatever has no name. In religion there's God. Wall Street has its own *It*. There's something funny about the whole thing. I believe *you* when you tell me I'm famous, but that doesn't mean I digest the idea to the point of believing *it*. Besides, who can feel any respect for fame? The famous are the babies of the crowd. The crowd needs a single person to baby or to worship. Out of a dozen physicists they pick Einstein. But in matters like this, one cannot speak about oneself. I don't feel myself. I'm numb about myself."

"But here we are fifty years after the Armory Show, which you didn't even see, and you're invited to lecture about it in Utica and New York . . ."

"Where's the distinction in that? Who doesn't lecture about art today? The entire art scene is on so low a level, is so commercialized — art or anything to do with it is the lowest form of activity in this period. This century is one of the lowest points in the history of art, even lower than the eighteenth century, when there was no great art, just frivolity. Twentieth-century art is a mere light pastime, as though we were living in a merry period, despite all the wars we've had as part of the decoration."

"But anyway, it's you they invite to lecture."

"Oh, you know what that is. Up until about ten years ago I was known as somebody who hadn't produced for a long time, a has-been . . ."

"A glamorous has-been."

". . . and then along came Abstract Expressionism and 'pop' art, and they brought some of my old attitudes into consideration again. For instance, when I left my old studio on Fourteenth Street I sold my icebox to Tinguely. It was an excellent icebox. What has Tinguely done with it? He's wired it for sound, and it was in the 'New Realists' show at Sidney Janis'. It's the appeal my old 'ready-mades' have for young people. They love me as providing a kind of *raison d'être* for their own ejaculations."

"Ejaculations?"

"In the French, or purely physical, sense. As for the Abstract Expressionists, they liked things of mine like the *King and Queen Surrounded by Swift Nudes*, figures in which there is nothing recognizable anatomically speaking. Of course, Abstract Expressionism is just a kind of 'second wind' of Kandinsky, Mondrian, and, perhaps, Kupka around 1910. And pop art is just a 'second wind' of Dada. I was never a real Dadaist; I wasn't in Zurich when Tzara and the others began it in 1916. But Picabia and I did something similar to it. Nothing new, of course. The spirit of Jarry and, long before him, Aristophanes — the antiserious attitude, which simply took the name Dada in 1916, that's all. By the way, Picabia's coming back, you know, like everybody else. He was *very* talented and clever, a real painter."

"Weren't you with the Picabias the famous weekend in 1912 when Apollinaire read his poem 'Zone' that he had just finished?"

"At Gaby Picabia's mother's house in the Jura. Apollinaire wrote awfully foolish things about art, but he was a charming man. He looked like the photographs I see of Oscar Wilde. The weather was terrible. He read 'Zone,' and we played a lot of Jack Straps.

"Jack Straps?"

"Sorry, Jack *Straws*."

"Thank you, Marcel. And your last word for the readers of *Show* is . . . ?"

"That's easy. Beware of artists. Artists are beasts."

"All artists?"

"All artists since Courbet have been beasts. All artists should be in institutions for exaggerated egos. Courbet was the first to say 'Take my art or leave it. I am free.' That was in 1860. Since then, every artist has felt he had to be freer than the last. The Pointillists felt they had to be freer than the Impressionists, and the Cubists freer still, and the Futurists, and the Dadaists, and so on and on. Freer and freer and freer — they *call* it freedom. Drunks are put in jail. Why should artists' egos be allowed to overflow and poison the atmosphere? Can't you just smell the stench?"

An Approach
to James Jackson Jarves

This was a preview, written for The Magazine of Art *in 1948, of my biography* The Two Lives of James Jackson Jarves.

On the fifteenth of November, 1851, James Jackson Jarves, a young American of thirty-three, wrote from Paris to his friend R. C. Wyllie, Minister of Foreign Relations of His Majesty, the King of the Hawaiian Islands, in Honolulu:

My dear Wyllie — I find myself settled at last in this city of cities, for how long, the future only knows — it is needless for me to say that I enjoy my residence — My only regret is that I did not come direct here when I left the Islands in 1848 — It would have saved the loss of my fortune. . . . My business, agent for purchasing for a certain house in Boston, promises fair — at all events it is a safe one. . . .

Jarves, the eldest son of Deming Jarves, the inventor of

Sandwich glass, had first gone to Hawaii in 1837, as a delicate youth of nineteen, to escape the rigors of New England weather. There he had lived with one or two interruptions for eleven years, first acquiring (with money advanced by his father) a silk plantation which failed, later combining his duties as Director of the Government Press and editor of a newspaper, *The Polynesian*, with partnership in a not supremely prosperous general merchandising business and the writing of two books: *History of the Hawaiian or Sandwich Islands* and *Scenes and Scenery in the Sandwich Islands*. After leaving the Islands he lost his "fortune" in another commercial venture in San Francisco and was appointed vice-consul for Hawaii in Boston and a Special Commissioner of the Hawaiian king to draw up treaties of "friendship, commerce and navigation" with the governments of the United States, Great Britain and France. Jarves' name appears in the United States–Hawaii treaty of 1849, but he never acted for Hawaii with European governments. When in 1851 he set sail, for the first time, for Europe — the climate of Boston was always to be too much for him — his official ties with Hawaii were ended, and he was what he described himself as being in his letter to Wyllie, "agent for purchasing for a certain house in Boston." A rash house, one can only think, considering Jarves' far from brilliant previous record in commerce.

But purchasing for Boston was not long Jarves' activity in Europe. Probably aided by the success of his Hawaiian books, especially the history, which had gone into several editions, he had secured entrée to *Harper's New Monthly Magazine*, and in it he published a series of humorous, brash little sketches of the Paris scene later issued by Harper's as a book, *Parisian Sights and French Principles, seen through American Spectacles*, in 1852, with a second series three years later. And in Paris Jarves did something else, something that proved to be fatal: he visited the Louvre.

> I ask every cultivated American what are his sensations as those treasures of Art, in which Europe abounds, for the first time open upon his intellectual vision? Does he not feel

the same sense of expansive joy . . . which the dweller amid crowded streets feels, when he also for the first time rambles forth into the country, breathes the fresh air, and gazes upon the wondrous variety of nature? . . . All persons whose hearts are not made callous by ignorance, vice, or familiarity, are keenly susceptible to the eloquence of nature. The first interview with true art produces a movement of the soul scarcely less spontaneous and deep, when we abandon ourselves with equal confidence to its influence.

So Jarves subsequently wrote in one of his books aimed at familiarizing Americans with art, and the sentences are eloquent of the agitation caused in him by his own first art exposure. For to art, when he entered the Louvre, Jarves had indeed been a stranger. "My prior experiences were derived solely from years of travel in virgin-soils," he wrote, "where Art was either as unknown as the mountains of the moon, or but a feeble exotic." The only previously seen picture of which he had a vivid recollection was his first, "a *Coronation of Napoleon I,* which we saw when eight years of age. Our first impression was to wonder how a flat surface could be made to present such an appearance of projected figures." Within a few months after that "first interview with true art" Jarves had left Paris and taken up residence in Florence; and there, seemingly with almost no delay, he began to imitate the example of another visitor to Florence of whom he writes: "I have known a friend, who proposed, on his arrival, to limit himself to a few cheap copies, carry away nearly one hundred original paintings." He wrote later: "I was a born collector. As soon as promoted to the dignity of pockets, I collected shells, then minerals, coins, Indian relics, rare books, and whatever America in my boyhood had to offer that was strange and interesting to one of my means and opportunities." In Florence his reading of Rio, Lord Lindsay, and Ruskin aroused in him a particular enthusiasm for early Christian art, and that was the art that he began principally to collect. He began, as he himself later pointed out, none too soon:

> Within the memory of those now living, gold background pictures, of the schools of Giotto and his successors, owing

to the contempt the pseudo-classical French taste had excited for them, were brought out of suppressed churches
and convents, and publicly burned to obtain the trifling
value of gold which remained in the ashes. Amateurs are
now more inclined to pay their weight in gold for the few
that have escaped the ravages of time and Vandalism, and
the same government which permitted this destruction, in
1859, sequestering all in public buildings as national property, passed stringent decrees to prohibit their leaving the
country.

A light is thrown on Jarves' sensibility and on the beginning
and the trend of his collecting by another passage from one
of his books:

> A distinguished poet beautifully illustrated to me, one day,
> the tenderness of kindred Art. He had collected many speci-
> mens of the works of the early religious painters of Italy,
> quaint and dry in execution, but, injured and time-worn as
> they were, full of deep meaning. Upon my inquiring why
> his taste led him to purchase pictures which the present age,
> in the pride of its science, despised, he replied, that . . .
> respect for the minds that produced them prompted him to
> take them to his own home, as an asylum from modern
> ignorance and scepticism.

During the seven years between 1852, when he arrived in
Florence all but ignorant of art, and 1859, when he transported
his possessions to America, Jarves bought the more than a
hundred pictures, chiefly of the Tuscan schools of the fourteenth and early fifteenth centuries, which form the collection
bearing his name in the Yale University Art Gallery. It was
an absorbing quest:

> . . . My adventures in this pursuit were often curious
> and instructive. They involved an inquisition into the intri-
> cacies of numberless villas, palaces, convents, churches, and
> household dens, all over this portion of Italy; the employ-
> ment of many agents to scent out my prey; many fatiguing
> journeyings; miles upon miles of wearisome staircases; dusty
> explorations of dark retreats; dirt, disappointment, fraud,
> lies and money often fruitlessly spent; all compensated,
> however, by the gradual accumulation of a valuable gallery.
> . . . On one occasion, to get nine pictures, I was obliged to

purchase a gallery upwards of two hundred; the unnecessary ones being sold at auction in England. . . . In the lumber room of a famous convent I chanced upon a beautiful Perugino, so smoked and dirtied as to be cast aside by the monks, who, for a consideration, gladly let me bear it away, and which upon cleaning proved to be untouched, and one of his finest compositions. . . .

It is interesting that although the esthetic level of Jarves' paintings is extraordinarily high, testifying to his taste and esthetic concern, and although in his art books Jarves would freely discuss esthetic principles, still whenever he spoke to Americans about his collection he tended to emphasize other considerations, as in the following passage from a letter, now in the Library of the Boston Athenaeum, to Charles Eliot Norton: "Beside illustrating the progress of painting in Italy, my object has been also to show the development of the Christian idea in art, getting together for that purpose, as great a variety of pictures as possible. Thus, besides its artistic and esthetic value, the gallery should possess an historical and religious one. Hence not the least of its importance is its consecutiveness in these several aspects." The outstanding beauty of the pictures, however, leads one to suspect that the enthusiastic and susceptible collector, in moments of private contemplation of his treasures, when he was not paying his respects to the thirst for instruction and Christian edification on the part of a possible contemporary public, may not have so minimized esthetic considerations.

Not content with enjoying and collecting these wonderful old things with which he had so recently become acquainted, Jarves felt compelled to tell his compatriots about them. Since his arrival in Italy he had been writing chiefly additional travel sketches for *Harper's*, later collected as *Italian Sights and Papal Principles* (1856), but in 1855 appeared, both in New York and in London, the first of his art works, *Art Hints*, with its missionary preface:

I have, myself, too strongly felt the need of a work which should embrace both the abstract principles and rules of Art and an outline of its historic progress and social relations, not to believe that a book comprising these facts and ideas, in a popular form would be useful. . . .

My object, however, is to treat of Art as a *whole,* embracing its general relations to man, not minutely, but in a suggestive form, and more as an aid to, than as forestalling inquiry. . . .

Art has much to hope in her future from England and the United States. Their political institutions, diffused education, wealth and mental activity, are so many guarantees for its rapid development. On the other hand, in the zeal of commercial activity, the haste of production, the impatience of realization, and the despotism of fashion, there is a danger to Art.

Art Hints could be described as a handy compendium of art history, Renaissance history, art practice, and esthetics; it was written, Jarves said, "in the fervor of a fresh intellectual enjoyment," and it is a lively book, containing a good deal of autobiography, purple writing, and enthusiasm. It was a new variety of art writing, especially novel in being an American product, and as Jarves said, "On account of its earnestness, it met with a kind welcome, both in England and America." Despite the callowness of some of its judgments, later acknowledged by Jarves, it is astonishing to think of its having been written by someone who had barely seen a picture a few years before.

Those years of Jarves' first residence in Florence were a heady period for the convert who had previously lived in "virgin soils" innocent of art. He wrote not only *Art Hints* and the book of Italian sketches, but also an amusing, sparkling pseudoautobiography entitled *Why and What am I?* and a novel, *Kiana,* based on a Hawaiian legend; and by the time he left for the States in 1859 he had almost completed his second art book, *Art Studies,* a survey of Italian art illustrated by engravings of his own pictures. He had become a friend of Mrs. Browning, Mrs. Jameson, The Trollopes, Seymour Kirkup, Walter Savage Landor and other members of Florence's British colony; he had visited and corresponded with Ruskin and Rio, become acquainted with Charles Eliot Norton, and corresponded with Longfellow and Emerson. The collecting of pictures became a passion to which all else was sacrificed. He engaged in no business. He had persuaded his mother, whose favorite child he seems to have been, that a collection of Italian paintings was a sound investment; and through her intercession with his father he was advanced sums of money against his anticipated share in the estate. This aroused resentment in his brothers and sisters, who feared for their patrimony. His wife, with whom his life had never been comfortable, was frequently hysterical on the subject of the collection; the money he poured into it, she claimed, left her without funds for servants or food or clothing; and one of Jarves' daughters has childhood memories of hating the pictures because her mother did, because the children were ordinarily kept out of the best rooms in the house (which had been turned into picture galleries) and because her nurse had the habit of leading her up to a picture of Saint Jerome and threatening to feed her to his lion if she failed to behave.

Jarves' object in transporting his pictures across the Atlantic in 1859 was certainly in part his expressed desire to a form "a museum of olden art for America, based upon a chronological and historical sequence of paintings, arranged according to their motives and technical progress"; but it was equally certainly in part a desire to recoup, by disposing of the pictures (but only to the proper person or institution), the money which he had spent on them. That, given his financial circumstances, was the only way he could continue collecting!

In *Art Studies* there is an ominous forboding of the difficulties to be encountered in the achieving of that dual object:

> "Old masters" are almost a byword of doubt or contempt in America. . . . It is the more important, therefore, that they should be fairly represented among us, by such characteristic specimens as are still to be procured.

"A byword of doubt or contempt"! It was all too accurate a forecasting of Jarves' tribulations, lasting over a decade, with his pictures in his native land — a country which at that time possessed not a single art museum of any importance. If old masters in general were suspect, how very particularly so were most of those in Jarves' collection — those stiff, unfamiliar, early, primitive, and pre-Raphaelite pictures of a kind hitherto almost never seen by Americans! His troubles in placing his collection form the best-known part of Jarves' story. The first exhibition in New York in 1859–1860, with controversial, often scathing, mentions in magazines and newspapers; the attempt, led by Charles Eliot Norton, to secure the pictures for the Boston Athenaeum; the failure of that attempt due to apathy, distaste, and doubt; the subsequent exhibitions in Boston and New York, with Jarves stoutly refusing to sell pictures singly except for a few disposed of to cover expenses, and with the miscarriage of a series of prospective sales of the collection (for a time there was talk of its acquisition by W. W. Corcoran); the loan of $20,000 to Jarves by Yale in 1868, the pictures forming the security and being hung in the new art school building of the university; Jarves' inability to redeem the pictures in 1871 and their final, reluctant acquisition by Yale at auction, in the absence of other bidders, for the additional payment to Jarves of $2,000.

The sorry saga left Jarves with a lasting and understandable resentment toward America. His first wife, left behind in Florence, died there in 1861; in 1862 he married again, and after the close of the Civil War (in which one of his sons had been wounded) he sailed with his new wife to live again in Florence, his home, although he made frequent trips to the States, for the rest of his life.

But Jarves' resentment toward America was expressed chiefly in admirably constructive, positive forms. In his third art book, *The Art Idea*, published during the war, he devoted much space to criticism of American artists, and there are numerous passages (appreciated by Lewis Mumford in *The Brown Decades*) expressing confidence in American art and admiration for her clipper ships, for the newly laid-out Central Park, for the shop windows and other features of American cities. *The Art Idea* went into several editions, and in 1869 Jarves' fourth art book, *Art Thoughts*, also contained both praise and blame of art in his country. His *A Glimpse at the Art of*

Japan (1876) has caused Bernard Berenson to say of him ". . . he was the first American, indeed perhaps the first white man to write sympathetically about the art of the Far East." He wrote occasional articles on art for American magazines, chiefly *Harper's* and the *Atlantic,* and in 1880 he was appointed American vice-consul in Florence. Two years later he was defeated in his attempt to be appointed consul by the organized opposition of embattled American artists resident in Florence, who were resentful of his openly expressed low opinions of their work as compared with that being done by Europeans. A second collection of paintings made by Jarves is now in the Cleveland Museum of Art, a collection of textiles in the Farnsworth Museum at Wellesley, and in 1881 he presented a collection of Venetian glass to the recently founded Metropolitan Museum in memory of his father. In his last years he did considerable European purchasing for the Metropolitan — some of his acquisitions of contemporary Italian sculpture make one sympathize with the resentment of the American artists in Florence — and he was on good terms with its officials and trustees. "We have just returned from Chicago and the West," he wrote to his son Horatio in 1882 in one of his last letters to be preserved. "Vanderbilt sent me passes for all his roads, wh. was a pleasant gift, under the circumstances — the Trustees of the Met. Museum give me a dinner before embarking, as I am their agent in Europe."

Jarves was never a wealthy man, and he tried constantly to augment the income which in one way or another continued to come to him from his family and the income of his second wife by investing in commercial enterprises, which almost invariably turned out to be disappointing. He had the Midas touch in reverse — or so it seemed during his lifetime. In after years the story changed. "It is fortunate," Frank Jewett Mather, Jr., wrote erroneously in an article in the *Yale Alumni Weekly* for May 22, 1914, "that he [Jarves] died a bachelor. Had he left children, Yale would morally owe them the price of two or three stadiums." The attention of one of Jarves' daughters — the one who had been threatened with sacrifice to St. Jerome's lion — was called to Professor Mather's article, and in a letter to the director of the Yale University Art Gallery she ruefully declared that she would be content to receive — if only circumstances allowed her to be offered — the present market price of any one of the pictures. Circumstances did not allow.

Jarves is an attractive figure, standing out, among his American contemporaries, above both the businessmen who crowd the scene and the more academically connected of the art lovers and critics — such as Charles Eliot Norton, whose long friendship with Ruskin began with their introduction by Jarves in 1855 and who never wavered in his admiration of the collection. Despite financial stringency, a tendency to querulousness and combativeness, an unhappy first marriage of more than twenty years, and the long rejection of his pictures, he retained until late in life a capacity for an idyllic *joie de vivre* that many of his more conventionally "distinguished" compatriots either did not possess or did not indulge. In 1884, at the age of sixty-six, he wrote from Fiesole in a letter to General di Cesnola, the director of the Metropolitan:

> Back of us are the old Etruscan walls; before us Florence, the val d'Arno & the villa-clad Apennines — Near the site of one of Cicero's villas — archaeology, history, art and the poetry of nature around and above us on all sides — The girls have improvised moonlight dances in the superb loggia and among the trees and flowers, to the music of guitars, mandolins, etc. played by the gentlemanly contadini, whose music, manners and dancing are alike charming. . . .

And the same relish for living is evident in *Italian Rambles* (1883), the best pages of which are as infectious as the Italian writings of Norman Douglas.

But later in 1884 Jarves lost one of his chief sources of joy, his youngest son, aged fifteen, a gifted artist. His beloved second wife died in 1887 and he himself the next year. His last writing was published posthumously in 1891: *Pepero, The Boy Artist: A Memoir of James Jackson Jarves, Jr., by his father.*

Long forgotten, except by an occasional art historian or recorder of Americana (his name means nothing to most visitors to his pictures), Jarves is far from deserving of his oblivion. In the United States, as Lionello Venturi has said, it was he who "first created a collection dedicated mainly to Italian painters, with a selectivity remarkable for his time, or for any time, and with definite ideas concerning the cultural purposes of art collecting. . . . Jarves is the real type of the pioneer in the field of Italian art." Even among Americans who have come after him, few have been, as he was, thus doubly preeminent as collector and — to use a word that ill expresses his apostleship — as critic.

A Letter
from Stockholm:
The Return of Christina

Queen Christina of Sweden makes a brief but dramatic appearance in the memoirs of the Grande Mademoiselle, that rich and maritally frustrated first cousin of Louis XIV; and after the publication of my biography The Grand Mademoiselle *(1956) I was tempted to follow it with one of Christina. That book was never written. But Christina casts a spell; and in 1966, when the Council of Europe arranged an exhibition in Stockholm reassembling many paintings and other objects from her famous art collection, I wrote the following account for* The New Yorker.

September 1966

So accustomed does one become here in Stockholm to the courteous facility with which Swedes speak English that it is no surprise to come upon Queen Christina herself doing so, in the guise of Greta Garbo. At present, the beautiful Garbo face

and singsong Garbo voice can be enjoyed over Swedish sub-
titles several times a week in the theatre of the Nationalmuseum,
as portions of the 1934 Hollywood film *Queen Christina* are
shown in connection with a vast exhibition called "Christina,
Queen of Sweden — a Personality of European Civilization."
Needless to say, the film makes few concessions to historical
fact. Indeed, its chief effect when seen in these circumstances
is to demonstrate invincibly the greater dramatic possibilities
of true biography over the fictionalized variety — unless the
fictionalizer happens to be Shakespeare.

The exhibition is a triumphant reconstitution of one of the
strangest personalities in history — the northern Protestant
princess who became queen of her grim, frigid realm at the
age of six, after her father, Gustavus Adolphus, fell on the
battlefield of Lützen in 1632, during the Thirty Years' War;
who abdicated the throne when she was twenty-eight, em-
braced Roman Catholicism, and lived the rest of her life
in self-imposed, luxurious exile in Rome, entertaining scholars,
artists, princes, cardinals, and the Pope himself, never abandoning her title or privileges as queen; and who amassed in her
palace on the Tiber one of the most famous ensembles of paintings, drawings, sculptures, coins, medals, manuscripts, and
books in the history of collecting. The success of the exhibition
is due to the skillful choice and presentation of more than fifteen hundred documents, works of arts, costumes, and other
objects that either belonged to Christina or were associated with
her life. The exhibition is divided into two sections — "Christina's Life" and "Christina's Collections" — and as one passes
from room to room, her story unfolds and her personality
grows evident, assuming grandeur as one reaches the halls
containing those portions of her collections that have been
reassembled for the exhibition. (During the centuries since
her death, they have been widely dispersed; for example,
Agostino Caracci's *Martyrdom of St. Bartholomew* has been
lent by the Maharaja of Baroda.)

Christina's exotic taste as reflected in the exhibition causes
a shock even in the sophisticated Stockholm of today. The

Nationalmuseum stands on the bank of the Norrström, one of the city's many waterways, opposite the ferries for Finland and the other white shipping of this busy port, and backing onto a tree-lined estuary that shelters a multitude of small craft. The water is chilly even in summer, the air crisp, the northern light sharp and silvery. On glassed-in café terraces, one drinks *akvavit* and enjoys herring or crayfish garnished with the fresh dill that in Sweden is as customary as parsley in America. When one leaves these bracing surroundings for the museum rooms, everything changes. One enters a meridional world of sumptuous velvets, of unclad nymphs and languorous goddesses, of voluptuous scenes that radiate the golden light of Italy. There are canvases by, among others, Titian, Tintoretto, Veronese, and Parmigianino; drawings by Michelangelo, Raphael, and Bernini (who was Christina's great friend); illuminated manuscripts and rich bindings and brilliant majolica.

In studying Christina, one seeks in vain some early influence that would satisfactorily explain the violent deflection from her northern environment. It is well known that, following her father's instructions, she was brought up to be as little womanly as possible, and with such success that when Louis XIV's cousin, the Grande Mademoiselle, first saw Christina in France at the age of twenty-nine, she described her as resembling "a pretty little boy." Her childhood tutor in Stockholm, Johannes Matthiae, a tolerant theologian, was largely responsible for her considerable learning. He saw to it that she spoke French, German, Italian, and Dutch, as well as Latin, and later she acquired a smattering of Greek, Hebrew, and Arabic. She was always passionately interested in literature and science. But her other tastes were more obscurely inspired. At the age of five, she wrote to her father, absent on his campaigns, "Please bring back something beautiful." It was not until she was in her twenties and governing her country that anything beautiful, in an artistic sense and in any quantity, found its way into the medieval fortress that Stockholm Castle was in those days. In 1648, the Swedes captured Prague, and included in the booty slowly sent north by pack train were almost a thousand paintings and sculptures from the collection that had been assembled by the Holy Roman Emperor Rudolf II. Some of these Renaissance masterpieces delighted the mannish young queen. One sees from a letter she wrote about them that her preferences in this direction had been formed even earlier: "Apart from some thirty or forty Italian originals [actually, a few were copies], I discount them all. There are works by Albrecht Dürer and other German masters whose names I do not know but who would arouse the profound admiration of anyone other than myself. But I do declare that I would exchange them all for two Raphaels, and I think that even this would be doing them too much honor." (Some years later, Christina acquired not two but several Raphaels — a Madonna, and five predellas from an altarpiece in Perugia. Today, the altarpiece is owned by the Metropolitan Museum, and one of its missing predellas, once Christina's and now borrowed from its present owner, the National Gallery in London, is in the exhibition in Stockholm. She gave away, to Philip IV of Spain, two magnificent panels by the disdained Dürer — the Adam and Eve that hang in the Prado.)

The arrival in austere Sweden of those Italian pictures — those glowing canvases, some of which are currently revisiting Stockhold in the exhibition — fanned the flame that had somehow been ignited in the breast of this strange young woman whose fame had already spread across Europe, who presided over councils, who informed her ministers that she would never marry, who conversed with ambassadors in their own tongues, who observed dissections, who invited the philosopher Descartes to Stockholm (where he literally perished of cold), and who accepted from Pascal the gift of one of his famous calculating machines, ancestor of the computer. She nurtured within herself a love for warmth, for color, for the sun — a longing for the south, and, heretically, for Rome. Quite early, she began secret correspondence with the Vatican, hinting at the possibility of her conversion. (Later, she facetiously told the Lutheran court chaplain, a certain intolerant and intolerable Erik Gabrielsson Empora-grius, that it was his person and his sermons that had driven her to Rome.) She had been deliberately brought up to be willful, her own master, and some historians see in this the germ of the appeal of Rome — the "free will" of Jesuit theology, as against the Lutheran and Calvinist predestination.

In the current exhibition, the room presenting the Stockholm court as it came to be under Christina's rule shows an immediate change from the earlier, often gauche exhibits. The faces of courtiers, now depicted by portraitists summoned from France, begin to look human, and even charming. For Christina's coronation, which took place when she was twenty-four, special embroideries and medals were imported. She dispatched agents to buy antiquities. In letters to Rome she asked endless questions about cultural life there. Then, at the age of twenty-five, she announced to the Privy Council that she had decided to abdicate. Faced with their dismay, she reconsidered, but three years later, on June 16, 1654, she irrevocably stepped down in favor of her cousin Charles Gustavus. That same night, she left Sweden.

Her progress southward was a series of pageants. In Brussels, she secretly confessed to the Catholic faith. In Innsbruck, she was publicly converted to Catholicism in the castle chapel. The princes and cardinals of the Italian towns along her route vied in staging spectacles of welcome. In Rome, the receptions in honor of the illustrious convert were of almost hysterical magnificence (Bernini was commissioned to redesign the Porta del Popolo in her honor), and her first lodging was in the Vatican itself, where she was confirmed by Pope Alexander VII. After several temporary residences, she settled for the rest of her life in the Palazzo Riario, by the Vatican bank of the Tiber, in what is now called Trastevere. In the eighteenth century, the Palazzo Riario was largely reconstructed as the present Palazzo Corsini. At the rear, this palazzo looks upward to the pines of the Janiculum, and the scene is much as it was in Christina's day, when her casino stood approximately on the present site of Garibaldi's equestrian statue. The Palazzo Corsini now houses a national picture gallery. This contains few pictures relating to Christina, but it does incorporate, intact from the old Palazzo Riario, the room in which Christina died, on April 19, 1689, at the age of sixty-two. Orange marbleized columns separate the room into two parts. (One part held Christina's bed.) Its windows look out on a typical Trastevere street of ochre stucco houses. And on its walls hang two of the gallery's greatest treasures — Caravaggio's *Narcissus* and his *St. John the Baptist*. They never belonged to Christina, but they are worthy of her, and were painted by someone with a personality as bizarre as her own.

During the nearly forty years between her abdication and her death, Christina lived an ample life. She had been allowed to take with her from Stockholm many of the Italian pictures from the Prague spoils, and now she enlarged her collection. She organized and presided over "academies" of artists and scholars, she sponsored concerts and theatricals, she entertained visiting notables and cardinals by the score, she did much reading, and even a little writing. (Her favorite form of composition was the maxim, inspired by the maxims of La Rochefoucauld, also a great political nonconformist, whom she met on one of her visits to Paris.) However, hers was by no means a serene existence, nor would she have wished it to be. "I love the storm and fear a calm," she once wrote to Cardinal Mazarin, Louis XIV's prime minister. She was far from a model convert. Particularly at this moment of the Counter-Reformation, she was, owing to her rank and fame, an acquisition highly valued by the Church. But Christina as a Catholic rather reminds one of Picasso as a Communist; too great a prize to be reprimanded, she proved an embarrassment nonetheless. Unpredictable and wholly *sui generis*, she constantly indulged in theological disputes. When Church dignitaries solemnly praised her as a glorious bulwark of orthodoxy, she was apt to retort that they were mistaken. "My religion is that of the philosophers," she said on one occasion. "I prefer this to all others."

There is one hideous episode in her life that stands apart from theological niceties and puts her forever beyond the moral pale. A plot was hatched by Mazarin to detach the kingdom of Naples from France's enemy, Spain, and set it up as an independent realm. Mazarin encouraged Christina to think of herself as the future Queen of Naples. She traveled to France to urge the matter on. Suddenly she discovered that her own equerry, the Italian Marchese Monaldeschi, had leaked the plot to Spain. She was at that time living, as the guest of the King of France, in the palace at Fontainebleau. She summoned Monaldeschi into her presence, together with a priest, her captain of arms, and several soldiers. Confronted with proof, Monaldeschi begged for pardon. Unmoved, Christina asked the priest to "prepare this man for death" and left the room. Monaldeschi made his confession and was slaughtered then and there — the execution was difficult, since he was found to be wearing a shirt of mail. Guides at Fontainebleau still show tourists a spot in the Galerie des Cerfs that they claim to be the stain of Monaldeschi's blood. Nothing more clearly reveals Christina's character than her reply to Mazarin's outraged protest over this assassination: "Personally, I find it far less difficult to strangle people than to be afraid of them. As for my treatment of Monaldeschi, all I can say is that if I had not done what I did I would most certainly not go to my bed tonight without doing it. I have no cause for regret, I have every reason to be pleased. Such is my opinion of this matter. If it gratifies you, I am glad; if not, I will nonetheless continue in it. For all my life I remain your very devoted friend, Christina." According to Swedish law, she had absolute rights over her own household, and Mazarin's remonstrances cloaked what was chiefly a concern that the supremacy of the King of France in his own land had been breached. Nevertheless, although Christina continued to be treated with outward respect by the French court, she soon returned to Rome. The Naples dream was over. By her barbaric act she had created around herself an air of dread that all her refinements of taste, so manifest today in this splendid exhibition in Stockholm, could not quite dispel.

Even so, Christina was the first foreign ruler to be buried in the nave of St. Peter's, with ceremonies that rivaled those that had welcomed her to the Eternal City. In 1965, her grave was opened, and a cast made from her silver death mask is displayed here in Stockholm. It confirms the evidence of the innumerable portraits — a heaviness of feature, protuberant eyes, large nose, and ironic mouth: no beauty, but a presence imposing, spirited, and highly intelligent.

Museums and exhibition committees these days compete with each other not only as to shows but as to catalogues. For historians and specialists, even the bare listings that served as collection catalogues in former times make fascinating reading, but the exhibition catalogue as a literary form is a comparative newcomer, a phenomenon of our day. The work of teams of scholars, with each item not only listed and described but assigned its historical significance, a modern exhibition catalogue is a compilation that can rival the most serious works of history. The Christina catalogue, with its more than six hundred meticulous pages — printed in two illustrated editions, Swedish and English — is an admirable achievement, certain to be of permanent value.

A Letter
from Florence:
After the Flood

While writing the biography of James Jackson Jarves, a Florentine by choice, I learned something of the beauties, both open and hidden, of that enchanting city of his adoption, and have often returned to see more. One visit, whose nature I hope may never be repeated, paid in January 1967, is recounted in the following pages, first published in The New Yorker.

January 1967

The plain on both sides of the Arno which is today the site of the city of Florence was said by Livy to have been so marshy in antique times as to have impeded Hannibal during his march on Rome, and according to Florentine legend it took Hercules himself (whose effigy appears in one of the ancient seals of the city) to drain the swamp and make possible the founding of a settlement. The plain has had to be kept drained ever since, and, even so, the Arno has frequently flooded over into it; there have been about sixty floods of various degrees of gravity since the twelfth century, the worst until now having been those of 1333 and 1844. The summer tourist, who often sees the Arno at Florence as a stony river-bed, can scarcely be expected to imagine its sinister potentialities.

If Hercules had been available to repair the results of the mammoth inundation of November 4, 1966, the worst disaster in the annals of the city, his task would have closely resembled another of his exploits — the cleansing of the Augean stables. Today, more than two months after the event, men and women in high boots are still shoveling out of cellars and other low-lying places in various quarters of Florence deposits of greenish-gray, malodorous mud left by the receding Arno, and, along with it, debris of all kinds — tree branches, other people's furniture, clothing, window frames, splintered bric-a-brac — that landed blocks, or even miles, from its place of origin after being swept along at astonishing velocity (up to thirty-five miles an hour) by the water in the streets. And everywhere one sees another characteristic souvenir of this most modern of floods — the smeary brown-black stain of oil, which came from thousands of smashed fuel tanks and was carried on the surface of the flood. In many places, there is a high-water line of oil along a gray or pale-yellow Florentine façade; in others oil coats an entire surface — a door, the panes of a window or a row of windows (sometimes second-story windows) — and even the insides of houses and shops.

A visitor to Florence today is impressed not only by the magnitude of the disaster but by the recuperative energy of the Florentines. In the center of the city, the section best known to tourists, shops that had been completely devastated began reopening as early as three weeks after November 4. Friends and relatives helped shovel out mud and fallen plaster, contractors were persuaded to give precedence, and ruined stocks were replaced by wholesalers in Rome and Milan — or, in the cases of the small specialty shops for which Florence is famous,

215

by local embroiderers and other home craftsmen. By now, attractive lighted shop windows alternate with still-vacant establishments that either are in the process of being reconstructed or remain (usually behind a cleaned-up façade) in a state of ruin, depending on the character, the means, and, often, the age of the shopkeepers. Some older merchants have given up — especially those numbed by the double loss of what was a combined shop and dwelling — but most of the younger proprietors, some of whom live on the outskirts of the city in modern apartment houses that were unscathed, have taken full advantage of the government subsidies, low-interest loans, and foreign aid to which they have access. The resuscitated shops all exhibit a thoroughly Italian regard for appearance; there are few "business-as-usual" compromises, the establishments having been completely restored to their former glory through unimaginably rapid feats of cleaning and painting.

By Easter, at least as far as façade is concerned, tourist Florence is expected to present an almost normal appearance. The three largest and most central hotels — the Savoy, the Grand, and the Excelsior — all suffered ruined basements, heating systems, kitchens, and ground floors, but they all plan to reopen by April 1; the museums and the churches, cleaned though scarred and many of them far from whole, are open already. At the Opera, the floor is still carpetless and there is a high-water stain along the walls and straight across the beige velvet curtain, but on a recent cold Sunday afternoon the performance of Donizetti's *Don Pasquale* was sparkling, and a *"programma preliminare"* of the spring music festival was being distributed. Everywhere, the great enemy now is mold. Walls, including those hastily replastered, are breaking out in spots, and everyone mentions *"l'odore di muffa."* The extent of flood damage to foundations throughout the city is as yet unknown. With warmer weather, foundations will dry out more or less and then will or will not crack.

It is not in the streets lined with shops that one realizes most clearly the hardships wrought by the flood. Four and a half thousand families lost their homes. Especially around Santa Croce and in the poorer districts of San Frediano and Gavinana, one sees row after row of empty, gutted flats on the first and second floors of tenement buildings; often entire houses, weakened by the flood, have had to be vacated, and numbers of them have been propped up with timbers, which close some of the narrower streets to traffic. Many families of slender means in these districts were provisionally moved to not yet completed city housing on the outskirts of the city. The municipality and private aid have given them subsidies, a little furniture, and, according to present ruling, three rent-free months. By the end of that time, it is hoped, their old homes, many of which were never very solid, will be dried out and repaired. Only forty or so Florentines died in the flood, but most of the deaths took place here in these tenements, where it was hardest to escape being trapped. One still sees more mud and oil here than elsewhere. The people evacuated were generally the lowest paid of all Florentines, ground-floor and second-floor rents being the most modest in the city, and now, because of flood damage to the companies that employed them, they are the most apt to be out of work. They are the indispensable hard-working "little" Florentines whom one reads about in the novels of Vasco Pratolini, and a consciousness of these dispossessed pervades the city. It is omnipresent, like the mold, and like the remains of the mud, which, even in the most carefully cleaned sections of Florence, has penetrated every crack, so that whenever rain comes, out it still oozes.

No official warning was ever given to the population, and although the river had been badly swollen for days, most Florentines slept through the night of November 3–4 ignorant of the imminent danger. The mayor has declared that he and much of his official family were on watch throughout the night, keeping in touch by telephone as long as they could with engineers upriver; that the river was constantly expected to subside; and that when, on the contrary, it began to spill over into the city in the early-morning hours, it was already too late, and warning by loudspeaker, klaxon, or the tolling of bells would have brought only panic. Some Florentines were awakened during the night by telephone calls from friends in the country who were alarmed by the appearance of the upper Arno; others, out late at night, drew their own conclusions from looking at the river. But not even the fire brigade or the military in local barracks was officially alerted.

The only Florentines to be warned as a group were the jewelers with shops lining the Ponte Vecchio and the streets adjoining it. These merchants employed a private night watchman. At about one in the morning, he telephoned to the homes of those whom he could reach, and a number came, unlocked their shops, and filled suitcases with what they could, the bridge trembling beneath them. Others, in the absence of any official warning, thought that their watchman was exaggerating, and went back to sleep. The jewelers who did come had to leave quickly; the water was already close, and, in addition to the trembling, there were frightening sharp reports, as though the bridge were cracking. The wife of one of the jewelers has said that when she and her husband arrived they found a number of noctambulous Florentines — some of them apparently hoodlums, some in cars with headlights pointed toward the scene — gathered at the end of the bridge, watching, as though hoping to see it break and collapse. The arrival of the jewelers with their suitcases was greeted with jeers. Two policemen were also standing there watching, and when the jeweler's wife angrily asked why they weren't out spreading the alarm, their answer was "We have no orders." The water continued to rise, and about half the jewelry shops on the Ponte Vecchio are now gaping open — gutted by the tremendous force of a torrent that passed right through them. The worst damaged are those on the east side of the bridge; they took the full brunt of the current.

The flood damage to Florence has frequently been spoken of as "worse than the war." Apart from the physical differences of the two catastrophes, there can, of course, be no real comparison between deliberate destruction planned and executed by man against his fellows and a totally unlooked-for accident of nature. Even in the latter case, however, people are disposed to fix blame, at least for negligence. The knowledge that one small group of citizens was warned has done nothing to diminish the outcries of other Florentines, and charges are being loudly made in advance that the official investigations now under way will provide nothing but whitewash. But out of the mass of lamentations, accusations, and so-called "evidence" that inevitably accumulates in the wake of such a disaster, a few details seem to be incontrovertible. First, the position of Florence is obviously a highly vulnerable one. At the bottom of a bowl of hills, it is watered by a river that during periods of rain and melting snow has always been swollen by tributaries from the deforested mountains among which it flows before reaching the city. One of these mountain tributaries, the Sieve, is particularly dangerous, and has given rise to a Florentine proverb: *"Arno non cresce se Sieve non mesce"* — "The Arno doesn't rise unless the Sieve rushes into it." The only way to be sure of avoiding Florentine floods, someone has said, would be to move Florence. Then, there is the question of dams. The abrupt opening of a hydroelectric dam at Levane, thirty-eight miles above Florence, on the night of November 3 and the consequent release of millions of tons of water certainly aggravated the height and force of the flood. The dam apparently would have burst if it had not been opened, but some hydraulic experts believe that it could have been opened earlier and more gradually. At any rate, the timing of the opening of the dam at Levane and the degree of cooperation and communication that existed between the dam engineers and the officials of the great city downstream are naturally being much discussed in Florence and throughout Italy at this moment, with greatly varying proportions of information and misinformation. A resurgence of the traditional Italian lack of confidence in governmental protection has reminded people of the years of flooding in the valley of the Po, the rate at which Venice is sinking into its own canals, the dam disaster at Lungarone, and last year's landslide at Agrigento, caused by overbuilding. In such matters, the philosophical and stoical Italian acceptance of disaster is, ironically, thought to have contributed to official neglect. "This famous patience of ours has become a vice," one Italian remarked the other day.

The lack of official warning in Florence was followed, for a time, by a strange playing down of the extent of the disaster over the nationally owned Italian radio and television stations. A day or two after November 4, one newscaster announced to a public still uninformed of the extent of Florence's submersion that "the situation in Florence is returning to normal." Premier Aldo Moro, when criticized in Parliament a week after the disaster for not having yet visited the stricken city, made a reply that has become famous: "My fourteen-year-old daughter is up there, helping save the books from the National Library."

Before very long, the national government did order soldiers to help clean up, and, together with the municipality, granted small subsidies which were fairly quickly paid — about thirty dollars to each householder for one room devastated and something less for each additional room, and, to each shopkeeper or artisan who could prove loss, up to half a million lire (about eight hundred dollars). The national government has also guaranteed ten-year bank loans at three percent interest. But distrust of the government persists, and many Italians have hesitated to contribute to the government's flood-relief fund, fearing that the cash will go *"dentro il calderone"* — "into the pot." Quite typical is the preference displayed by one of the largest hotels in Rome, which inquired directly of one of its Florentine opposite numbers what was needed most, and, upon being told that it was a pump, sent one by truck to the Florentine hotel's door. And when the employees of that same Roman hotel decided to contribute one day's wages to Florence (the management matched the total of its employees' gifts), the money was taken straight to the Florentine hotel and divided among eight of its employees who had lost their homes and belongings. There are countless stories, many unverifiable, about refusals of foreign aid-in-kind for purely bureaucratic reasons — the variety of red tape most commonly mentioned is the imposition of customs duties on donated articles — and it is certain that much of the actual money aid coming from foreign sources is being, and will continue to be, distributed by nationals of the donor countries, either directly to the needy or, if through official Italian organizations, quite carefully, on the basis of results previously accomplished.

As for the casualties in paintings, books, manuscripts, and archives, one of the reproaches constantly heard since the flood has concerned the storage of so many of the city's treasures in low-lying places. The ancient printed volumes of the Palatine Collection, which were presented to the city in the eighteenth century by one of the last of the Medici, were kept in the basement of the Biblioteca Nazionale Centrale, a building constructed in this century — despite the warning provided by floods of other centuries — only a few feet from the bank of the Arno; these are the most celebrated of the millions of Florentine books that were immersed in water and emerged covered with mud and oil. The city archives, dating back centuries, are in shelves on the ground floor of the Uffizi, and the lower three or four shelves of the archives, including documents from the thirteenth century, were water-soaked. One reply to the reproaches on this subject is a reminder that at the time of the *last* Florentine disaster, the artillery bombardment of the city in 1944, the danger came from above, and at that time it was the treasures kept on *upper* floors that caused the greatest concern. Certainly it has been common for at least a generation now to think of safety as lying underground, man having become accustomed to regard himself, rather than nature, as his most likely destroyer.

The Uffizi Gallery has now reopened, and is featuring an exhibition entitled *"Dipinti Salvati dalla Piena dell'Arno"* — "Pictures Saved from the Arno Flood." The pictures, which were in the process of restoration in the Uffizi Restauro, in the basement and on the ground floor, were brought upstairs in time, early on the morning of November 4. More than two hundred paintings on wood panels, including about forty that were not moved out of the Uffizi Restauro in time, are at present being treated, across the Arno, in the Boboli Gardens' *limonaia* — a vast greenhouse where the Gardens' hundreds of lemon trees usually pass the winter. (This year, they have been moved into a sheltered courtyard of the nearby Pitti Palace.) Inside the *limonaia*, on both sides of a long center aisle, as in a military hospital, are rows of metal frames with pictures lying prostrate on them like so many casualties on their beds. The patients are bandaged wholly or in part with rice paper, which holds the pigment down while the wood panels dry out. Each panel bears a tag like a fever chart — a carefully inscribed record of its decreasing degree of humidity. Overhead rumbles a huge machine that was rushed from Rome to control the humidity in the *limonaia*. Men in white jackets — the staff of the Uffizi Restauro — work on those pictures that have dried out sufficiently to be touched; with pincers they peel off the rice-paper bandages and perform other delicate operations. Squatting on the ground under the pictures are students — some of the thousands from all over Europe who converged on Florence in a sort of mass winter-vacation pilgrimage. Talking together in various languages or combinations of languages, the students apply liquid preventives against mold to the undersides of the panels. Many of the medicines being administered to the pictures are toxic; the restorers and the students have been ordered to wear gas masks, but the order is often ignored, and there have been a few cases of illness from the fumes.

The largest, and also the most gravely maimed, of the patients in the *limonaia* is the great Cimabue *Crucifixion*. For many years, although it is the property of the Franciscan friars of the Church of Santa Croce, which stands in a particularly low-lying part of the city, it hung in the Uffizi, up several long flights of stairs; a few years ago, the friars asked that it be returned to them, and they hung it in their museum, on the ground floor off their cloister. Among the most striking photographs of Florence at the height of the flood was one taken from the air that showed the cloister of Santa Croce filled with water nearly up to the top of its arcades; here the flood water was at its highest, remained longest, and left the most mud. The official statement is that the Cimabue is "seventy percent destroyed." What is not said is that the seventy percent includes almost the entire body of the Christ. Looking along the immense crucifix from the head as it lies on metal trestles in the *limonaia*, one can discern the form of most of the body in light-colored bare wood — or, rather, in a thin layer of what seems to be canvas, applied to the wood before the paint was laid on. The paint used for the body seems to have been the most vulnerable. The present opinion is that, for the most part, the picture is not restorable, and that it should be rehung, in its tragic state, as a memento of the flood, with, beside it, a photograph of it as it came down from the thirteenth century to November 4, 1966.

For centuries, students of the Italian Renaissance in all of its aspects have come to work in the libraries of Florence. These are the world's richest in this field — in printed books, manuscripts, and archives. Of them all, the Biblioteca Nazionale Centrale is the greatest — along with the library of the Vatican, the most renowned in Italy. The flooding of the Nazionale and of other Florentine collections of books and documents has been, apart from human losses, the greatest blow suffered by the city. Florence's continued usefulness and reputation as an international scholarly center depend on the rapid recuperation of the damaged collections. It is estimated that close to two million volumes need restoration, including rebinding, before they can be returned to use. Drying out is the first step. Many of the water-soaked volumes are being interleaved with blotting paper at various treatment centers in Florence, and others are being given first aid — some of it necessarily a little rough — all over Tuscany and Umbria. Near Arezzo, some of the lofty barns used by the Italian state tobacco monopoly for the drying of tobacco leaves are now full of volumes hanging over poles, with tobacco-leaf care-takers acting as book nurses; brick factories, textile-drying sheds, and even heating plants have been pressed into service. In a hall of the Certosa, a Carthusian monastery a few miles outside Florence to which in summer busloads of tourists go to see the sights and buy the liqueur made by the monks, a blower has been installed to dry out some of the two hundred fifty thousand water-logged volumes of the Gabinetto Vieus-seux, a polylingual lending library and reading room that occupies ground-floor and basement quarters in the Palazzo Strozzi. The Certosa has lent the space out of deference to Count Tardini, president of the Gabinetto Vieusseux, a num-ber of whose ancestors lie buried in the Certosa graveyard.

At the Baptistery, facing the Cathedral, five panels of Ghiberti's bronze *Gate of Paradise* were detached by the flood, and they have not yet been reinstalled. Inside the Baptistery, the other day, a pretty blond girl kneeling, head bowed, before the altar was found to be not praying but, rather, brushing from its sculptured marble panels a dusting of talcum powder with which she had earlier sprinkled it as one of several steps in the removal of its coating of black flood oil. All over Florence, the winter-vacation students (the girl in the Baptistery was from the University of London) have been helping de-mud and de-oil sculpture that had pre-viously gone uncleaned for generations. Certain sculptures have emerged from their unaccustomed baths in a new guise; of the four horses in Ammanati's Neptune fountain beside the Palazzo Vecchio, for example, two have turned out to be of white marble and two of porphyry, instead of a general gray, as they had long seemed to be. The cleaning of large numbers of lesser sculptures often reveals the preferences of the cleaners; girls from all over Europe lovingly clean every square inch of the innumerable cupids, whereas stern, bearded Jupiters — harder to clean, anyway, because of their dense marble curls — are often neglected.

A hundred and fifty young people — principally from Italy, England, the United States, Holland, and Germany —

have formed a group called Centro Operativo Firenze, with headquarters at present in a Via Ghibellina *palazzo* whose lofty rooms are empty except for cots and the few mud-caked belongings of the workers. These people have undertaken to do the hardest and most repugnant job of all, the emptying of mud-filled cellars, and are still receiving about forty requests a day from all over Florence. Their long days are spent heaving pails of stinking silt from icy, black basements up onto the streets, where the deposits are eventually taken away by the army, to be dumped outside Florence. For a short time after the disaster, this frightful task of cellar-cleaning was performed by the army itself, under government orders. The high-spirited boys and girls on whom the job has now, unfathomably, devolved are paid a tiny stipend by the Commune of Florence and are fed, appropriately, in an orphanage.

The countless anecdotes one hears in Florence about "what I did the day of the flood" remind a New Yorker of those he has heard about "what happened to me during the blackout," and, indeed, the Florentines, who know all about that night in New York and have read about the population increase nine months later, are fond of saying, "What's going to happen here? We were without electricity for three weeks!" Dry Florentine humor has produced a number of flood jokes, sardonic, self-deprecating, often anticlerical. Like all disasters, the calamity attracted many curious out-of-town sightseers, and when the Pope came from Rome to say a midnight Mass on Christmas Eve it was remarked, "So even His Holiness has dropped in to see what the Boss has been up to!"

Ten thousand automobiles are said to have been ruined, or nearly ruined, in the flood. (One of the macabre effects of the rising waters was to short-circuit automobile wiring, causing the horns of drowning cars suddenly to start blowing and their headlights to flash on.) Florence has been suffering for many years from a plague of automobiles in its narrow streets. For a time after the flood, automobiles were barred from many areas, and lovers of the city hoped that the prohibition might be continued, at least in part. Now, however, except for streets closed for reconstruction or sewer repair, all traffic restrictions have been lifted, and once again the city is choked; the absence of not a single one of the ten thousand damaged automobiles can be noticed.

Walking along the Arno these days, the visitor from abroad is apt to realize that his eyes turn upward less often than they used to toward the hills around Florence, with their woods and villas and castles. Instead, his attention is riveted to the devastated riverbanks and, above all, to details of walls. The action of the water and subsequent hand-scrubbing have caused the lower stories of many buildings to emerge a lighter color than the rest — below the dreadful, ever-present high-water line, which is already commemorated by a number of engraved plaques. Often, it appears, the oldest buildings — and the oldest furniture as well — resisted the flood best. Surveying the damage, one lover of this city (which was a massive fortress before, and even while, becoming an art center) remarked, "If Florence weren't so ancient, it wouldn't still be here."

Translating
Madame Bovary

In 1957, on the occasion of the publication by The Modern Library of my translation of Madame Bovary, *the following pages, a kind of translator's memoir, were printed in* The New York Times Book Review.

"Writing is a lonely occupation," says the cliché; but it must have been invented by a nonwriter, or by some novelist or biographer or translator as a joke. For even on days when the persons one is inventing don't get off the ground they seldom abandon one to the point of loneliness; and when one grapples with men and women who have already lived, or who have previously been invented by a master, the hours are full and flying.

During the year or so I spent translating *Madame Bovary* there was much time when I was alone with Emma and her fellow beings. Indeed the bulk of the work was done in that kind of "solitude." But every once in a while there arose a puzzle that called for consultation, and the "solitude" would be broken by a phone call, a letter, or a visit. I appealed — appealed for information or confirmation; and the generosity of the response would have cured a misanthrope. The following are a few lines of tribute.

Early in *Madame Bovary* Flaubert describes the laden dinner table at a house party in the château of a Norman marquis. Then he adds a brief sentence: "*Mme. Bovary remarqua que plusieurs dames n'avaient pas mis leurs gants dans leur verre.*" Keeping in mind that Emma was much impressed by her surroundings that night, and that the French "*remarquer*" is sometimes a little stronger than the English "remark" or "notice," and that at such a dinner in France the "*verre*" probably wasn't a water glass, and that whereas French syntax calls for "*verre*" in the singular English requires the plural, and that English prose has rhythms different from French rhythms, a fair equivalent for the original seemed to me to be: "Madame Bovary was surprised to notice that several of the ladies had failed to put their gloves in their wineglasses."

All very simple — one of the simpler sentences in the book to translate — though there remain a few little points both in French and English that specialists could argue about if they wanted to.

That was what Flaubert wrote. But what did Flaubert mean? Why should Emma Bovary have expected all the ladies to put their gloves in their wineglasses? Why was she surprised that some of them didn't?

The full answer was hard to come by. Mademoiselle Gabrielle Leleu, of the Municipal Library at Rouen, who has helped me solve many a Flaubert puzzle, was herself puzzled by this one. "Many ladies drank wine in France at that time," she wrote me. "I don't see why they should have, as you suggest, been expected to put their gloves in their glasses to indicate to the *sommelier* that they wanted none — the equivalent of putting one's hand over one's glass, or turning the glass upside down, today."

The first help came from Oberlin, Ohio. "Having read in Sunday's *New York Times* . . . that you are doing a new translation of *Madame Bovary*, I am taking the liberty of sending you some notes I had printed for the use of my students . . .": so began a welcome letter from John C. Lapp, then professor of French at Oberlin. The "notes" proved to be a veritable *Madame Bovary* dictionary and encyclopedia combined, and here I found a quotation from one of Alfred de Musset's plays, ironically listing the things a young girl of 1836 must do to be in the swim: "Does she put her gloves in her glass when the champagne comes around? . . . If she doesn't know enough to do that, she hasn't learned very much."

And then the road to the full, completely clear solution was shown me one day by Douglas Cooper, the art historian. "Why don't you write to the painter Jean Hugo at his farm in southern France?" he said. "He's full of knowledge of nineteenth-century customs." I followed his advice, and back came a note from Jean Hugo, enclosing one from a friend whom he had consulted, the Vicomte de Noailles:

> A hundred years ago it was generally held that a woman who was *comme il faut* never drank wine. But I think that in respectable provincial society this must have been much more the case than in the more advanced court circles, at the Tuileries, for example. Probably among Normandy squireens the most provincial still held to the custom, and Flaubert had been struck by the fact that in such circles as that of the Princesse Mathilde it had come to be ignored. Still, even in my own youth I saw the Comtesse Murat, who was a bit affected in that she never drank champagne, put the lace-edged handkerchief she carried in her hand into the *flûte de champagne* when she sat down to dinner. Remember: Women didn't have handbags in those days.

So it all became clear. Emma, in expecting all the ladies at table to put their gloves in their glasses, was following, in her own genteel, young-lady way, the custom observed by her provincial though noble hosts, and followed by most of their guests. But among the company were a few who were more "advanced" — they had probably come down for the house party from Paris — and those ladies surprised Emma by their freedom. The party at the château, Flaubert is telling us, even though glamorous to the provincial Emma, was in itself provincial. It's a good thing to know the precise meaning of what one translates. And this time it was good to know that the rendering of *"remarqua"* by "was surprised to notice" was justified — in fact, called for — and that the *"verre"* was unquestionably, and so very interestingly, a *verre à vin!*

Later when I recounted the puzzle of the gloves in the glasses at Bernard Berenson's Villa I Tatti, near Settignano, Nicky Mariano laughed. "You should have come straight to me," she said. "I could have told you." I assured her that I would the next time. But if I had, I wouldn't have had the final paragraph of the Vicomte de Noailles' letter, which I like as much as what preceded it: "The wine question is very close to the cheese question. I once heard Madame de Chevigné say: 'In my youth a woman who was *comme il faut never* ate cheese.'"

A Proustian footnote: for Madame de Chevigné, the Vicomtesse de Noailles' grandmother, was one of the models for Oriane, Duchesse de Guermantes.

And then there was the question of Madame Bovary's piano. When she played "with dash," Flaubert says that *"les cordes frisaient."* "The strings ———": what did they do? The word *friser* has so many meanings, the most common, of course, being to curl — frizz — one's hair. But did the strings curl up? Unlikely, especially since Flaubert goes on to say that the piano could be heard "to the end of the village." Dilemma. I took it to Theodore Steinway, and this time it was he who wrote to France. His colleague there knew perfectly well what Madame Bovary's piano did: it jangled. I'm grateful to those two gentlemen, for Mansion's two-volume French dictionary doesn't breathe the word "jangle" under *"friser"* (Fr-Eng), or the word *"friser"* under "jangle" (Eng-Fr); and in those early days (this phrase, too, came near the beginning of the novel) I had not yet realized how many specialized meanings the big Larousse provides. Poor Emma!

Even her piano, one of her great sources of distinction, was a rattletrap.

And what about Binet, the grotesque bachelor with the passion for making wooden objects on his lathe, whom Madame Bovary calls on in her desperate quest for money? What does Binet have on the shelves of his room when Mme. Caron and Mme. Tuvache, the mayor's wife, spy on the interview from behind the laundry hung up to dry at a nearby attic window? He is engaged, they see, in turning out a hideous, nameless object — "a conglomeration of half-moons and of spheres carved one inside the other, the whole thing standing erect like an obelisk and perfectly useless." And on his shelves were "napkin rings, candlesticks, and *pommes de rampe*." *Pommes de rampe? Pomme* is apple, potato, almost anything round or roundish. *Rampe* is ramp, or stair rail. But *pommes de rampe?* The answer seems easy now that I have it, but I had to seek it on 116th Street.

"Finials," said James Grote Van Derpool, librarian of the Columbia University School of Architecture. Thank you again, Mr. Van Derpool. Could Flaubert have imagined anything that lent itself better than the knobs of newel posts to the unimaginable horrors of Binet's creative invention?

There were many such blessed informants. Charles Weatherill, the renowned tailor, who told me exactly what Flaubert meant when he said that the trousers worn by provincial worthies were of *drap non décati;* Dr. Harold W. Rickett, bibliographer of the New York Botanical Garden, who furnished the English equivalent of every plant name I offered him; Norbert Guterman, whose extraordinary sense of verbal equivalents helped me in many a tight spot; voices at the other end of the telephone, responding to my appeals from museums, from still-existing harness shops and livery stables.

Robert Graves once offered as his favorite mistranslation of all time the rendering of *"Le peuple ému répondit à Marat"* as "The purple emu laid Marat another egg," and it is, in part, to try to avoid laying such spectacular eggs as that that a translator bothers friends, acquaintances, and strangers.

Cautionary examples aren't hard to find in translations of *Madame Bovary* alone.

At the *mi-carême* ball, Flaubert tells us, Emma wore "a cocked hat over one ear" (*"un lampion sur l'oreille"*), but one of the current British versions of the novel has her dancing with "a Chinese lantern dangling from one ear" — too merry a picture by far. And Charles, the medical student, instead of singing songs "at student gatherings" (*"aux bienvenues"*), is made to sing them "to women who were always welcome."

When Doctor Larivière, at Emma's deathbed, says, *"C'est bien, c'est bien"* ("Yes, yes"), he is merely expressing more or less polite impatience with Doctor Canivet, whose circumstantial narration of the case is pointless now that Emma is beyond help. But I have seen a critical article in a worthy publication that renders the words as "Good, good," and interprets them as expressing Doctor Larivière's satisfaction in Emma's imminent death, a satisfaction reflecting Flaubert's supposed conception of his heroine as a character too sublime for this world.

And I remember with particular pleasure an early British translation of *Madame Bovary* that is embellished with a grandiloquent introductory essay by Henry James. James writes much about "the rich and the rare" in the book, and promises the reader many aesthetic joys. But what do we find in the English text, which James clearly didn't bother to read? For Flaubert's description of one of the wedding guests, *"un mareyeur de leurs cousins, qui même avait apporté, comme présent de noces, une paire de soles"* ("a fishmonger cousin, who had actually brought a pair of soles as a wedding present"), we find this equivalent: "a practical joker among their cousins, who had even brought a pair of boot soles for a wedding present."

A perilous job, translating! Enough to make one long to sink one's teeth into a good *filet de semelle!*

A Meeting with Cocteau

*This piece and the two that follow — "A Visit to Barbette"
and "In Search of True Cocteau" — mark three stages in my
involvement, if so it can be called, with Jean Cocteau. The
first describes my only encounter with the poet, a few years
before his death; the second recalls an episode of my investigations while writing his biography; and the third was written to
celebrate the publication of the book. The first and the third
were first printed in* The New York Times Book Review; *the
second appeared in* The New Yorker.

One day late in May 1959, when I was living in Paris, I received a card from the president and members of the Municipal Council, inviting me to attend, on Friday the fifth of
June, at 11 A.M., the inauguration of a monument erected to
the memory of the poet Guillaume Apollinaire "in the Square

Laurent-Prache, at the corner of the Place Saint-Germain-des-Prés and the rue de l'Abbaye."

I had had advance word of this ceremony, and passing the Square Laurent-Prache recently (it is the familiar, charming little cluster of chestnut trees and graveled walks tucked into an angle of the Church of Saint-Germain-des-Prés just to the left of the church as you face it) I had seen that inside the gate a new stone pedestal had been set up, inscribed with the words "A Guillaume Apollinaire, 1880–1918." Atop it, thick folds of gray plastic concealed what I knew was a sculpture by Picasso. Someone had already decorated the pedestal, in pencil, with the word *"merde."* Ordinarily that could be assumed to be the work of some nameless gamin or hoodlum, but since *"merde"* was one of Apollinaire's favorite words, I couldn't help wondering whether some admirer of the poet, a foe of officialdom like Apollinaire himself, hadn't passed by, and, aware of what was soon to take place, been inspired to add this happy touch in advance of the official ceremony.

As to Picasso's sculpture, I had heard a good deal about that, too. When Apollinaire died in 1918 (weakened by a war wound, he had succumbed to the influenza that was epidemic that year), he had left behind him a surrealist novel-autobiography called *Le Poète Assassiné,* toward the close of which a memorial to the dead poet-hero of the book is constructed by a friend of his, an artist-genius who is both painter and sculptor. The memorial in the novel is a surrealist one: it consists of a hole in the ground that reproduces exactly the poet's bodily form. It is literally "pure form." Now the painter-sculptor in *Le Poète Assassiné* bears the nickname *"L'Oiseau de Benin"* ("The Benin Bird"): commentators have pointed out that for a number of years during Apollinaire's long friendship with Picasso, this genius painter-sculptor had in his studio a bronze Benin bird (a work of African sculpture), and after Apollinare's death his friends and especially his widow, Jacqueline Apollinaire, had hoped that Picasso would provide some sculptured tribute to the poet's memory.

Indeed, Picasso himself had offered to do this, but, "having

a morbid Spanish fear of anything connected with death"
(at least, so went the story one usually heard), he had con-
tinually procrastinated, procrastinated for decades, for over
a generation. It was only now, finally, badgered into action
by Jacqueline, that he had come through, not indeed with a
made-to-order hole in the ground or some other surrealist
manifestation, not even with a bust of Apollinaire or some
other work expressly created in memory of his friend, but at
least with a sculpture, one of his more recent works (so it
was said: I had not heard which one): and he had donated it
to the city of Paris to serve as an Apollinaire memorial.

The only reason for my receiving an invitation to the un-
veiling of Picasso's gift was the fact that in connection with
some work of my own I had been seeing, in Paris, a number
of "*Apollinairiens*," people who either had been friends of the
poet or had made him a subject of study. It was one of these,
the author of a French biography of Apollinaire, who had
kindly had the card sent to me.

Among the people I had been in touch with — in this case
by correspondence — was Jean Cocteau, who was at that time
living in the south of France. In a newspaper I had read a
remark of Cocteau's to the effect that during the period of
Cubism, Cubist artists had not been at all free to express themselves as they wished; they were "punished" when they dis-
obeyed certain strict rules, and Cocteau and Apollinaire had
both been "summoned to appear before a Cubist tribunal" on
the charge of "stylistic deviation." Cocteau because of his dar-
ing, "non-Cubistic" use of a certain word in one of his poems,
and Apollinaire because in the stage-set for one of his plays
he had permitted the use of motifs "other than a bottle of
anis and a guitar, or a pipe and a pack of cards." (Juan
Gris, at the same moment, had been awarded official Cubist
approval for his "introduction of the siphon into painting.")

"So Apollinaire and I came up for sentencing," Cocteau had
ended his article, "and I assure you it was no laughing matter."
I had wondered, when I read that, what the grim sentence
meted out by the Cubist tribunal might have been, and via a

friend we had in common I wrote to Cocteau and asked him.

His reply, which came in an envelope postmarked "Saint Jean Cap Ferrat, Presqu'île de rêve," was a charming note written in brown ink. "Everything was serious at that time, the moment known as '*l'époque héroïque de Montparnasse*,'" it read, in part, "and a tribunal was a tribunal. An artist was summoned before it for the slightest infringement of the Aristotelian rules of Cubism." That was the closest M. Cocteau came to answering my question. The letter was signed "*Votre poète, Jean Cocteau*," the signature being followed by a star, the Cocteau emblem. There was a postscript: "It is the dictators of art who make possible the disobedience without which art dies" — one of the better Cocteau aphorisms, I thought.

By the time M. Cocteau's answer came, the day of the inauguration of the Apollinaire monument was close at hand, and in the note of thanks I mailed off to the "*presqu'île de rêve*" I wrote that I looked forward to seeing him at the ceremony on the fifth and hoped that he would allow me to introduce myself to him that day. Privately, I hoped I might be able to extract from him, when we met, the answer I had asked for. There was no doubt in my mind that he would be present unless he were prevented by ill health (he had recently been not very well, our friend had told me). As a young man, Cocteau had known Apollinaire; ever since, he had made much of that acquaintance; he was famous; and he was the only person even remotely connected with Apollinaire to have become a member of the French Academy. He would certainly be a guest of honor.

What was my surprise, therefore, to receive after a day or two a second, briefer, note from M. Cocteau, this one addressing me with flattering informality as a colleague and saying that due to his "various addresses," letters sent to him sometimes went astray, and that he had not heard about the ceremony on the fifth. "It would be very good of you," he wrote, "to advise the organizers of this and to give me a few details." It seemed to me that it would smack of impertinence for me to write to M. Cocteau again, to give him details that he should receive from an official source, so after I had "advised the organizers" (that is, telephoned my biographer friend who had had the invitation sent to me, and got his assurance that he would immediately telephone one of his friends on the Municipal Council: something had certainly gone wrong, he said), I sent a telegram to M. Cocteau. I said that he would hear almost immediately from the Council, which was counting on his presence on the fifth at 11 A.M.

By now there was only a day or two to go.

The morning of the fifth was fine, and inside the Square Laurent-Prache I found that quite a few Apollinairians had already shown their cards at the gate and were waiting around the shrouded sculpture on the pedestal (the word *"merde"* had been erased) for things to begin.

Among them were a number of now-venerable writers who had been friends or acquaintances of Apollinaire, including his truly close friend, André Salmon, and there was a lady professor who gave a course on Apollinaire at a French university. As we waited, a friend introduced me to this lady, and I offered her a compliment that proved to be anything but a success. I told her that I had recently enjoyed reading not only the published text of the lectures she had given during the first semester of her course the year before, but also notes on her still unpublished lectures of the second semester — quite copious notes, made by one of her students, who had lent them to me. *"Comment?"* the lady shouted at me — the entire conversation had to be carried on in shouts and shrieks, for a hearse had just pulled up at the portal of Saint-Germain-des-Prés a few yards away, and the bells in the tower above us were tolling loudly — *"Comment? Mes étudiants font circular leurs notes? On pourrait me voler mes idées!"*

As I was yelling indignant words of self-defense, probably something quite bald, like *"Je ne suis pas voleur, chère Madame!"* the bells abruptly stopped, and the Apollinairians in the square, quite numerous by now, turned as a man to stare at me in surprise. Luckily, the moment was cut short by the

237

arrival of a cluster of important-looking gentlemen in morning dress, clearly the delegation from the Municipal Council. As most of the assembled guests moved back to let the new arrivals take a position close to the pedestal, the group separated to reveal a dapper figure until then hidden in their midst and whom they now respectfully gestured into a place beside the pedestal itself. I recognized Jean Cocteau.

Just as I was reflecting how curious it was that but for a chance remark in a letter from a stranger the guest of honor might not be present, and I was picturing M. Cocteau receiving first my telegram, then a wire or telephone call from the Council, then packing a valise and being driven to the Nice airport and taking a plane to Paris, I saw, outside the wire fence that encloses the square, someone crossing the Place Saint-Germain-des-Prés, quite alone. A slender woman with auburn hair, elderly, but with a still-pretty face and trim figure to make one think what a lovely young girl she must have been.

I recognized Jacqueline Apollinaire, the "pretty redhead" whom Apollinaire had married less than a year before his death, whom he celebrated in one of his most famous poems, "*La Jolie Rousse*," who still kept, unchanged, the apartment they had shared, and whose persistence, it was said, was responsible for the memorial we had gathered together to inaugurate. No one, apparently, had been sent to escort her.

She entered the square and made her way to the pedestal. The officials shook her hand; Jean Cocteau kissed her on both cheeks, and then she took her place a few yards away with her old friend André Salmon. Close to the pedestal but not at it, they formed a second-string pair.

It was a signal from the crew of a sound-truck from the Radio–diffusion Française, parked outside the fence, that started the ceremonies. The president of the Council briefly welcomed the principal guests and the assemblage in general; then, raising his voice — and perhaps remembering that André Salmon, though at the moment less known by the younger generation, was, in the opinion of many, a finer, though cer-

tainly less sensational, artist than the Academician guest of
honor, besides having been a far closer friend of Apollinaire
— loudly presented, to listeners both present and to be reached
by airwaves, *"Monsieur* André *Cocteau de l'Académie Française."*

Cocteau's aplomb was complete. Not by the slightest flicker
or glance did he reveal that he had heard the gaffe; whipping
out from his breast pocket a sheet of paper so neatly folded
that I had supposed it was a handkerchief, he read a deft little
speech that sparkled from beginning to end. "To salute Apollinaire is to salute Picasso, whom Apollinaire compared to a
pearl"; "On November 11, 1918, Paris was all beflagged in
Apollinaire's honor" — a reference to Apollinaire's death a
few days before the Armistice; "He augments the list of that
sacred and glorious race of poets whose work so soon takes
precedence over themselves." It brought to my mind again the
speed with which I knew Cocteau had prepared himself: certainly within a few days, probably within a few hours, perhaps within a few minutes, he had written an elegant, if rather
glib, little speech for an occasion of which so recently he had
had no inkling.

André Salmon was introduced next. He was at that time
eighty-seven years old, from the start his voice trembled, soon
his text about his old friend began to ramble, in a few moments tears began to trickle down his rugged, Semitic face,
and shortly he burst into sobs and could read no more. Amid a
hush, someone quickly took the paper from Salmon's hands,
found the place, and finished the reading, as Salmon withdrew
and was comforted by friends. Jacqueline Apollinaire kissed
him, I noticed.

And then Jacqueline Apollinaire unveiled the sculpture. She
was introduced, stepped to the pedestal, said nothing — or if
she did murmur a few words, they were inaudible ten feet
away. She pulled a cord — the gray plastic once covering the
sculpture had been replaced, for the ceremony, by a kind of
white veil — and there stood, revealed, Picasso's gift. It was a
handsome, bronze, more than life-size head of a woman. I

recognized the sitter immediately. She was Dora Maar, a lady prominent in recent Picasso annals, whose double profile is seen in many a canvas of the 1940's: when Picasso knew Apollinaire, Dora Maar was probably not yet born. Certainly those rumors had been correct that had reported the "memorial" as having no express connection with Apollinaire. On one side of the pedestal, I now saw, were inscribed the words: "This bronze, the work of Pablo Picasso, is dedicated by him to his friend Guillaume Apollinaire, 1959."

At that moment, timed so perfectly that I wondered whether the crew of the radio truck had arranged matters with the curé, the bells of Saint-Germain-des-Prés once again began to clang: the requiem mass was over; the pallbearers with the casket emerged from the church, and a line of black cars was forming behind the hearse. The lady professor, seeing a policeman in the Place Saint-Germain-des-Prés asking people in a few parked cars to move, to make way for the funeral, began to screech: *"Mon chauffeur! Où est-il! Quel est cet enterrement? O que c'est agaçant! Chauffeur! Chauffeur!"* Hastily bestowing a few handshakes, she rushed off. The ceremony was over.

From the Square Laurent-Prache most of the guests made their way across the Boulevard Saint-Germain to the Brasserie Lipp, where the Municipal Council had invited everyone to an *"apéritif d'honneur."* There, in an upper room, I saw André Salmon seated in a corner with a couple of friends, one of whom I heard order for him not the *porto* that waiters were offering all of us on trays, but a cognac: the old poet looked tired and depressed, shaking his head as though in dismay and self-reproach. Elsewhere in the room, Jean Cocteau was surrounded by a growing throng.

Going over to Salmon, I presumed to say something about his having paid a tribute to Apollinaire that was recognized by everyone present as the finest moment of the day, but although one of his friends said, *"Vous voyez, Maître? C'est ce que nous disions,"* he grasped my hand feebly and shook his head. I took my leave quickly, fearing he might weep again.

I had hoped to be able to try once more for an answer to the question I had asked M. Cocteau in my first letter, and now I made my way over to the group around him — a cluster, chiefly of younger men, that seemed almost to constitute a separate little *apértif d'honneur* of its own. It took me some time to penetrate it, and then I found Cocteau speaking so vivaciously about the new Orpheus film he was writing that I simply listened with the rest. As I stood there, his frequent utterance of the name "Orpheus" vividly recalled a feature of his speech that I had but fleetingly noticed during its delivery. It, too, had made prominent mention of Orpheus, and of stars — *"les astres."* Somehow, although Apollinaire, too, like most poets, loved to speak of the stars, those in Cocteau's speech now began to associate themselves rather with those brown-ink stars appended as emblems to the signature "Jean Cocteau" in the letters from Jean Cap Ferrat; and his mentions of Orpheus in the speech — although Apollinaire, too, had loved Orpheus — seemed in retrospect to relate rather sharply to one or two Orpheus films by Jean Cocteau.

This impression — it was no more than that, strengthened no doubt by the strikingly non-Apollinairian, purely Picassian, character of Picasso's "memorial" — had the effect of stiffening my resolution. After all, I told myself, grotesque as the fact was, Jean Cocteau's presence today was partly due to me, and I would press for a reward. So, when he eventually broke out of the surrounding circle, I accosted him.

I murmured my name, identifying myself as the sender of the telegram. *"Le télégramme?"* M. Cocteau inquired, suddenly cold — almost, it seemed, suspicious. *"Quel télégramme?"*

"In reply to your asking me to tell the committee that your invitation for today had gone astray."

"Ah, ça." There were just those two syllables, uttered in a dry tone of boredom and displeasure. Was I being told that mention of the episode was in wretched taste? That like the gaffe about "M. André Cocteau" it should be treated as though it never happened?

"What were those sentences meted out by the Cubist tribunals?" I persisted. I felt surprised at how completely willing to make a nuisance of myself I had suddenly become. "What punishment did they inflict on you and Apollinaire?"

"*Ah, ça . . .*"

Once again, that was clearly going to be the only answer, and M. Cocteau was moving on. But then something happened. Several of the young men who had been clustered around him had followed him, like students after a favorite teacher, and they heard my words and seemed surprised and interested. "*Comment, Maître? Des tribuneaux Cubistes? On était jugé? Comment jugé, Maître?*" Several such questions were quickly put.

No longer the mere prey of a lone importunist, but once again the center of a sympathetic group, Cocteau freshened before my eyes. His expression lost its coldness, vibrancy returned to his voice. "*Ah oui, je vous assure. . . . On était puni . . . Voyez-vous . . .*" And he launched into a charming little lecture, almost word for word what he had written in the article I had seen and in his first letter to me. "Oh, yes," he ended, "in those days a tribunal was a tribunal. It was no laughing matter, I assure you. Apollinaire and I were punished."

"But punished how?" I cried, again. "The penalties — what were they?"

There was no indication that M. Cocteau had heard me. He glanced at his watch, murmured "*Je regrette . . . un rendezvous . . .*," bowed to us all, and quickly disappeared.

What might the answer to my question be, I wondered, standing there momentarily alone in the midst of the *apéritif d'honneur*, Cocteau having left and his young admirers dispersed? What punishments could have been decreed by Cubist tribunals to deviating artists? And why had Cocteau not replied?

Now I thought I knew the answers: and some of my guesses have since been confirmed, I am pretty sure, in allusions to artistic quarrels of the day that I have seen in letters written by Apollinaire. "Tribunals": of what could those have consisted except a few dogmatic artists and theoretical critics, probably lesser fry in both cases, discussing so-and-so's latest work around tables in a café and deciding that it had "fallen off," that it "wouldn't do"? And the "punishments," the "sentences": what could they have amounted to except omission of a name from articles, verbal ostracism by a clique, waspish words of exclusion: "Apollinaire! Traitor! Unworthy of the name Cubist! Out with him!" And, finally, as to Cocteau's refusal to answer my question: why *should* a question be answered if the asker of it is so discourteous, or so obtuse, as not to care or see that the answer cannot possibly be as brilliant or as interesting as the provocative statements that led to the question in the first place?

One does not *have* to consent to dampen one's fireworks, just to satisfy the dull curiosity of a stranger.

One more little episode stands out in my memory of that day. After the *apéritif d'honneur* and after the excellent lunch that some of us stayed for, I was leaving the Brasserie Lipp when I saw, a few yards away in the Boulevard Saint-Germain, the figure of Jacqueline Apollinaire, once again alone. In the past I had called on her in her apartment, today we had exchanged a few words at Lipp's, and now I hastened my steps and asked if I might walk her home. She said she would be glad to be accompanied — to this day I marvel that no one had offered, or had been detailed, to escort Apollinaire's widow to and from the ceremony — and we walked along together.

I congratulated her on the success of the day, and said that I thought Picasso's head of Dora Maar looked very well — as indeed it does — under the trees.

"Yes," she said, "it is very strong. It is made of bronze. *Ça durera plus longtemps que nous.*" And after those words — I couldn't decide how equivocal they were — she told me that she had hoped that Picasso would attend the ceremony — "He sent a telegram" — and that throughout the morning she had kept missing good friends of Apollinaire who should have been present and who might have been present had the inauguration taken place only a few years before — *"les disparus."* André Derain, Vlaminck, Max Jacob, Serge Férat — she named those and others.

"The principal thing," I said, impulsively, "is that *you* were — *are* —present, and so very beautifully so."

"Confess, Monsieur," she said, gaily, "that you were surprised, astonished, to find that after all these years 'La Jolie Rousse' hadn't quite lost *all* her looks."

I did confess it, and she gave me a smile that conveyed a coquetry whose charm I could well imagine enrapturing Apollinaire. "Don't worry about me," she said. *"Je mourrai en beauté!"*

(1965)

A Visit
to Barbette

I had been told that most people flying from New York to Austin, Texas, are apt to be en route to conferences with either legislators or professors (Austin being both the state capital and the seat of the state university), and that my mission — to talk with a gentleman who had rocked the international vaudeville world in the nineteen-twenties and thirties with a trapeze act he did disguised as a girl, to the music of Wagner and Rimsky-Korsakov — would not, even though he was Texas-born, be considered by Texans a sufficiently serious reason for visiting their state. I suspected at the time that my informant was not entirely correct, and my suspicion has since been confirmed. In Texas, there are quite a few vaudeville buffs, I have discovered, who are respectfully knowledgeable about the career of Barbette (as the gentleman I had come to see was known professionally). And since Barbette is the hero of one of the best essays on the nature of art written by Jean Cocteau, the French poet, novelist, dramatist, draftsman, and *cinéaste* — an essay not unknown in university circles — his name enjoys, thanks to that connection, academic prestige at Austin as well as elsewhere. It is true, however, that although some of those admirers knew that Barbette was Texas-born, it was generally unknown that he had returned to the state and was living in Austin.

It was in connection with Cocteau, whose biography I was writing, that I wanted to see Barbette, and the person who finally found him for me was a professor in Austin named Paolo Vivante — a Hellenist and Latinist I had once known in Tuscany — who had never heard of him before. I had obtained Barbette's address through friends of mine who spend the winter in Florida, near Sarasota. Someone had told me that Barbette was now associated with a circus, and although Ringling Brothers and Barnum & Bailey Combined Shows moved its winter quarters some time ago from Sarasota to Venice, I knew that quite a few retired circus people continue to live in Sarasota, and my friends learned about Austin from one of them. (The retired performers aren't the only traces of the circus remaining in Sarasota, it seems. "The circus tradition lingers here in a delightful way," one of my friends wrote me. "The high school in Sarasota offers, as one of its forms of extracurricular athletics, circus training of almost every kind, including high trapeze, etc., and one of its graduates is now the current Lillian Leitzel with the big show. I forget her show name — something very fancy like La Gloriosa instead of her own wonderful name of Vicky Unus. She comes of a circus family. Her father was the man who stood on one finger — therefore 'Unus.'") But when I wrote to Barbette in Austin (my friends' informant said that he used the name Barbette as a last name, and that his first name was Vander), he didn't answer, and, fearing he might not be there, I asked Vivante to drive over from the university and inquire. He found him there — "a very nice, delicate man," he wrote me, "rather reticent, and wondering whether or not to encourage you to come down" — and a few days later came a note from Barbette himself consenting to see me.

He was standing beside Vivante at the Austin airport when I arrived, one spring evening (I learned later that he had been nervous while waiting, and had remarked to Vivante, "I feel this is the arrival of the literary FBI"), and I was at once struck by his careful grooming. Almost everyone else within sight was dressed with the utmost casualness — there was scarcely a necktie to be seen — but Barbette was wearing a dark, well-cut suit, a white shirt, a striped tie, and a narrow-brimmed brown straw hat. When he took his hat off, his sandy hair was impeccably brushed. He was spare and very erect, with thin, almost pinched features. He looked like a very trim older-man fashion model, less than his age, which I knew to be a bit over sixty. But when he moved he seemed older; his gestures and his gait, which at first struck me as mincing, I saw were not quite that but curiously careful — stiff and a bit jerky. I had heard something about his career's having ended with an accident, and assumed I was seeing the result. Also noticeable were his irregular teeth and a white scar near his mouth. His first words after greeting me were about Vivante: "What a particularly elegant ambassador you sent me!" That startled me for a moment, for Vivante, classicist though he is, had adopted what was apparently the local style of dress in a big way, and had come to the airport wearing a rusty black T-shirt, blue jeans, and sneakers; the contrast between his appearance and Barbette's was striking. But Barbette put me right, and in a way that revealed his grasp of the authentic. "The most complete gentlemanly refinement I've met with in anyone since the Vicomte Charles de Noailles," he said. The French title rang out oddly in the Austin airport. Vivante, looking a bit abashed at the tribute to his manners, quickly suggested that we find my suitcase and get into his car. We did so, and at the Stephen F. Austin Hotel, after I checked in, we sat down in the coffee shop.

The Vicomte Charles de Noailles, I knew, was the gentleman who in 1930 had given Jean Cocteau a million francs to make his first film — the now famous *Blood of a Poet,* in which Barbette appears. The Vicomte and his wife, much interested in the artistic avant-garde, at the same time gave a million francs to Salvador Dali and Luis Buñuel to make a successor to *their* first film, *Un Chien Andalou.* The new Dali-Buñuel work, *L'Age d'Or*, which is nowadays often called the first Surrealist film, proved to be so antireligious, antimilitary, and generally shocking that after riots had broken out in the theatre the French police confiscated the reels, and there was talk of the Noailles' being threatened with excommunication from the Catholic Church. (That disaster was averted, but the Vicomte was expelled from his club, the aristocratic Jockey — a serious chastisement for a Noailles.) *The Blood of a Poet* also caused them some distress. For one scene, Cocteau had invited the two Noailles and a few of their society friends to put on full evening dress, sit in one of a pair of theatre boxes that had been constructed on the set, chat among themselves as the cameras turned, and, at a signal, break into applause. They all enjoyed the lark until they saw the finished work and discovered that what they were applauding was a card game that ended in suicide, which had been filmed separately. The Noailles and their friends absolutely refused to allow this to be released, and the scene in the boxes was done over, with professional extras and Barbette, he and the lady extras wearing Chanel evening gowns. (For Barbette, this was no new experience, since he always made his first entrance for his trapeze act dressed in a ball gown and wearing an ostrich-feather hat.)

The night of my arrival in Texas, in the hotel coffee shop, Barbette reminisced a little about the scene in the box. "Cocteau told me that I was substituting for the Vicomtesse de Noailles, whom I knew," he said, "but neither he nor she nor anybody else told me why. Sitting in the box, I tried to imagine myself a descendant of the Marquis de Sade, of the Comtesse de Chevigné, who was one of Proust's models for his Duchesse de Guermantes, and of a long line of rich bankers — all of which the Vicomtesse was. For a boy from Round Rock, Texas, that demanded a lot of concentration — at least as much as working on the wire." Famous though Barbette was as an acrobat at that time, he was as naïve about moviemaking as the others had been, and he shared some of their scruples. "I didn't see the film until a couple of years later, and when I did I was absolutely dismayed," he said. "Chanel told me afterward that before recruiting the extras and me Cocteau had suggested that the ladies in the box be a few of her mannequins, but, knowing the story, she had refused to lend girls — only dresses."

At the time *The Blood of a Poet* was made, Barbette — who was born Vander Clyde, at Round Rock, a few miles from Austin, on December 19, 1904 — had known Cocteau and much of Paris café society for several years. He had done his earliest practicing on a permanently stretched galvanized-iron clothesline in his mother's back yard in Round Rock. "My mother was a milliner by trade and famous in the neighborhood for the drawnwork and embroidery she'd learned from Mexicans," he said. "She was very artistic, and admired culture. The first time she took me to the circus in Austin, I knew I'd be a performer, and from then on I'd work in the fields during the cotton-picking season to earn money in order to go to the circus as often as possible. My mother told me I couldn't leave home until I finished high school, and that encouraged me to 'double up' — I was quick in class, and I graduated at fourteen. The chief thing I regretted not going on with was Latin — I'd had only two years of it. I read *Billboard*, and I went to San Antonio in answer to an ad I'd seen in it, inserted by one of the Alfaretta Sisters, World-Famous Aerial Queens. The other sister had died, and this one — in private life she was the wife of a blackface comedian billed as 'Happy Doc Holland, the Destroyer of Gloom' — needed a new partner for a trapeze and swinging-ring act. She told me that women's clothes always make a wire act more impressive — the plunging and gyrating are more dramatic in a woman — and she asked me if I'd mind dressing as a girl. I didn't; and that's how it began. From Alfaretta I went into Erford's Whirling Sensation, a revolving apparatus with three people; we hung by our teeth and did our opening number wearing big butterfly wings."

After that, Barbette said, he began to develop his own

single act, which he designed not as just an imitation of a woman's trapeze act but, rather, as an exercise in mystification and a play on masculine-feminine contrast, using trapeze and wire as, quite literally, his "vehicles." Cocteau was to see this as a parallel to the poet's use of words, and, in fact, poetry had played a role in Barbette's concept of his act. "I'd always read a lot of Shakespeare," he told me, "and thinking that those marvelous heroines of his were played by men and boys made me feel that I could turn my specialty into something unique. I wanted an act that would be a thing of beauty — of course, it would have to be a strange beauty." As part of the strangeness, he sought a name with a feminine sound that could also be a family name — hence Barbette. His act caught on quickly all over the United States, chiefly, he thinks, because of its surprise element — his revelation, at the end, of his masculinity — which to him was always only one part of the whole, and the William Morris Agency sent him to England, and then to Paris, in the fall of 1923.

"Paris was *the* experience," he told me. "As soon as I got to my little Hôtel Moderne, near the Place de la République, even before opening at the Alhambra Music Hall, I felt that I'd found my city. And at the theatre I could tell that the audiences appreciated all the little refinements I'd worked on so hard. As soon as I finished at the Alhambra, the producer Léon Volterra put me into his revue at the Casino de Paris, and there the most wonderful people began to come around to my dressing room. It was an American society woman, Helen Gwynne, who first took me up. She introduced me to her friends, most of them wealthy expatriates — the Harry Lehrs, the Berry Walls, the Elisha Dyers — and to Princess Violette Murat. Soon I was being invited out by Violette's French friends: Cocteau, Radiguet, the Noailles, Georges Geffroy (you don't know Georges Geffroy, the great decorator? He invented the modern Empire style), writers and painters and composers — people who sensed from seeing my act that we were artists together. The name of Volterra's revue was '*Il N'y A Que Paris*' — 'There's Only Paris' — and that's how

I felt. The magazine *La Nouvelle Revue Française* printed a fine review of my act by a French intellectual named Drieu la Rochelle. He said that the interest lay not in the acrobatics but in the beauty of the performer. He loved the difference between the way I looked and the 'fat, muscular, graceless females,' as he called them, whom one usually sees. But, of course, the most perceptive was Cocteau. He saw even more in the act than I had realized was there myself."

I was able to show Barbette a few passages about him that I had found in Cocteau's letters, and these pleased him by their enthusiasm. On November 14, 1923, Cocteau alerted his friend the Belgian music critic Paul Collaer to Barbette's Belgian debut: "Next week in Brussels, you'll see a music-hall act called 'Barbette' that has been keeping me enthralled for a fortnight. The young American who does this wire and trapeze act is a great actor, an angel, and he has become the friend of all of us. Go and see him, be nice to him, as he deserves, and tell everybody that he is no mere acrobat in women's clothes, nor just a graceful daredevil, but one of the most beautiful things in the theatre. Stravinsky, Auric, poets, painters, and I myself have seen no comparable display of artistry on the stage since Nijinsky." He wrote to another Belgian friend, "Don't miss Barbette. . . . Call on him and tell him I sent you. You won't be wasting your time. He's both a great acrobat and a discriminating reader, in close touch with contemporary writing." And on November 23 he wrote to two artist friends, Jean and Valentine Hugo, in the South of France, "The god of friendship has punished you for never being in Paris when we are. Your great loss for 1923 was Barbette — a terrific act at the Casino de Paris. . . . Ten unforgettable minutes. *A theatrical* masterpiece. An angel, a flower, a bird."

"The French paid me the supreme compliment of thinking I was somehow too good to be true," Barbette said. "One journalist walked unannounced into my hotel room one day, obviously hoping to find something unimaginable. I was lying naked on my bed at the time, my face smeared with a blackish skin-bleaching cream. 'Two-sexed on the stage and two-colored at home,' he wrote in his account of the visit, and he expressed amazement at seeing on my bedside table Joyce's *Ulysses*, Cocteau's *Le Grand Ecart*, and a book by Havelock Ellis. In another way, my lucky choice of name made French people think of me as one of themselves from the beginning." Thereafter, Barbette returned to Paris almost every year, playing at the Alhambra, at the Empire, at the Moulin Rouge, at the Médrano Circus. "Of course, Paris was the best place, but there were other amusing cities, like Berlin, Hamburg, Copenhagen, Warsaw, Madrid, Barcelona, and when I appeared in them, friends I'd made in Paris would often come, and we'd do the sights together." As he prospered, he traveled with "twenty-eight trunks, a maid, and a maid to help the maid." Except at the Médrano, where it was impossible to keep other performers from watching, he allowed only two people to look on from backstage during his act — his maid, in one wing, and the stage manager, in the other. "I would tolerate nobody else," he said. "I was well known to be a martinet."

I could believe that, especially since I'd noticed several little severities to which Barbette had subjected our waitress in the coffee shop — the harsh rejection of a smudgy plate, a biting sarcasm when the coffee arrived too soon. Luckily, she was a good-natured girl, who seemed to find such fastidiousness comical: she tipped me a wink when Barbette gave an exaggerated start and said *"Please!"* as she put down some spoons rather noisily. "Since those years in Paris, I've never been able to readjust to crudity," Barbette said. "I'm living temporarily with my sister here in Austin before joining a big show a few months from now. I'll not be a performer, of course, but a trainer, trying to give young present-day acrobats some faint idea of what a refined act can be. I have to say that, apart from my family, everything about Austin offends me. And I know I'll be lucky if in return for my very handsome salary I succeed in persuading a few young trapezists just not to chew gum during their act. Imagine!"

It sounded prissy, and I noticed a quizzical look on the face of Vivante, by whose Tuscan parents, I well knew, all the refinements — including the moral and intellectual refinement that led them into exile from Mussolini, and the refinement of nonsnobbery — were so taken for granted as never to be mentioned. But I knew what Barbette was thinking of, and I recalled some of the tributes that Cocteau paid him in the famous essay on his act: tributes to the flair and the supreme professionalism that had enabled him to make what might have been a mere stunt — and a distasteful stunt at that — into an "*extraordinaire leçon de métier théâtral,*" a work of art. "He walked tightrope high above the audience without falling, above incongruity, death, bad taste, indecency, indignation," Cocteau said.

Cocteau, who loved the circus and vaudeville, had always seen a resemblance between a tightrope dancer's performance before a public that was indifferent to the arduousness of his efforts and the multiplicity of his perils, and the painful creativity of the poet. In Barbette he found his best illustration. In his essay — which, like Drieu la Rochelle's appreciation, first appeared in *La Nouvelle Revue Française* — he tells of having a sandwich and a hard-boiled egg with Barbette one evening and then going with him to his dressing room at eight o'clock (although his act would not begin until eleven) and watching the conscientiousness of his preparations — "a conscientiousness unknown to French actors, and characteristic of clowns, Annamite mimes, and the Cambodian dancing girls who are sewn each night into their golden costumes." As Barbette stripped and began to strap on a leather girdle, some chorus girls pushed open the door and gave little screams at the sight. All the conventional decencies were observed — they withdrew, and Barbette threw on a bathrobe before going to the door to talk to them. Then came the making-up, and Barbette remained a young man, a "*drôle de jeune diable,*" even in his completed makeup, which was "as precious as a brand-new box of pastels, his chin enameled with something shiny, his body unreal, as though coated with plaster." It was only when he held some hairpins between his teeth and started to adjust his blond wig that he began to "imitate every last gesture of a woman arranging her hair." Then, as he stood up and began to walk in a certain way and put on his rings, there was transformation: "Jekyll is Hyde," says Cocteau. "Yes, Hyde! Because now I find myself frightened. I look away, put out my cigarette, remove my hat. . . . The door opens again. It is the girls, now not at all embarrassed; they come and go quite at home, sit down, powder themselves, talk about clothes."

Barbette could slip in and out of his woman's role at will, and even before the curtain went up he revealed his genius for quick back-and-forth transformations — one of the elements that made his act seem to take place "in the streets of dream," as Cocteau put it. His maid came in, helped him on with his dress, and curled the feathers in his hat. Then they all left the dressing room, and on the stairs leading down to stage level "Barbette is once again a boy, dressed up for a joke, tripping on his skirt and longing to slide down the banister. He is still a man as he walks about the stage inspecting his equipment, does leg exercises, grimaces at the spotlights, hoists himself onto wires, clambers up ladders. The moment the question of danger is disposed of, he is a woman again — a society woman, giving her salon a last-minute inspection before the ball, patting cushions, moving vases and lamps."

Then, watching from out front, Cocteau describes what the spectators saw: "The curtain goes up on a functional decor — a wire stretched between two supports, a trapeze, and hanging rings. At the back, a sofa covered with a white bearskin." On the sofa, between the wire and the trapeze parts of the act, Barbette was to do a little striptease as he removed his long evening gown. "A scabrous little scene," Cocteau calls it, "a real masterpiece of pantomime, summing up in parody all the women he has ever studied, becoming himself *the* woman — so much so as to eclipse the prettiest girls who precede and follow him on the program." And here Cocteau begins to talk of Barbette's act, and of other theatrical examples, as parables of the artifice, the "lie," that all art is. "Don't forget," he says, "we are in the magic light of the theatre, in this trick-factory where truth has no currency, where anything natural has no value, where the short are made tall and the tall short, where the only things that convince us are card tricks and sleights of hand of a difficulty unsuspected by the audience. . . . Thanks to Barbette, I understand that it was not merely for reasons of 'decency' that great nations and great civilizations gave women's roles to men. He brings to mind François Fratellini explaining to me, when I was exhausting myself trying in vain to get something out of an English clown engaged for the role of the bookmaker in *Le Bœuf sur le Toit*, that an Englishman would never make a convincing Englishman; and Réjane's remark 'When I play a mother, for example, I have to forget that I myself have a son. At other times, in order to put myself across the footlights I have to imagine that I am a man.' Such detachment, such labor!" Cocteau exclaims. "Such a lesson from a professional!"

It was some of that labor, I knew — some of the perfectionism that had made Cocteau see in his act a lesson to all artists — that Barbette was thinking of, and evoking, in his dainty references to "refinement" as we sat in the coffee shop, the refinement whose absence he deplored in the waitress, in Austin in general, and, in advance, in the young trapezists he was soon to train.

In the essay, Cocteau compares the cumulative effect of Barbette's perfect disguise and elegant stage entrance to a cloud of dust thrown in the eyes of the public. Bursting on the audience as a "ravishing creature," he "throws his dust with such force that from then on he is free to concentrate on his wire work, in which his masculine movements will help him instead of giving him away." Thanks to the "dust," the audience will see him not as a man, which in his acrobatics he obviously is, but as "one of those amazons who look so dazzling in the advertising pages of American magazines." Then comes the striptease and the "scabrous little scene" on the sofa — another bit of dust, for once again he is going to need complete freedom of movement as he swings out from the stage over the audience on his trapeze, hangs by one foot, pretends to fall, half the time staring upside down at the spectators, "with the face of a crazy angel." In none of those gyrations does he *really* look very feminine, but the greater part of the audience continues to think of him as such. The reason for Barbette's popularity, Cocteau thought, was that "he appeals to the instinct of many audiences in one, and people vote for him for opposite reasons. He is liked by those who see him as a woman and by those who sense the man in him — not to mention those stirred by the supernatural sex of beauty."

But perhaps Barbette displayed the subtlest artistry of all, Cocteau thought, in the masterly close of his act — once again a model, in its meticulous attention to detail, for practitioners of any art form, who well know the difficulty of strengthening their effects through to the very end, of remaining constantly at high tension while unwinding. "Imagine what a letdown it would be for some of us if at the end of that unforgettable lie Barbette were simply to remove his wig," Cocteau writes. "You will tell me that after the fifth curtain call he does just that, and that the letdown does take place. There is even a murmur from the audience, and some people are embarrassed and some blush. True. For, after having succeeded as an acrobat in causing some people almost to faint, he now has to have his success as an actor. But watch his last tour de force. Simply to re-become a man, to run the reel backward, is not enough. The truth itself must be translated, if it is to convince us as forcibly as did the lie. That is why Barbette, the moment he has snatched off his wig, *plays the part of a man*. He rolls his shoulders, stretches his hands, swells his muscles, parodies a golfer's sporty walk. . . . And after the fifteenth or so curtain call, he gives a mischievous wink, shifts from foot to foot, mimes a bit of apology, and does a shuffling little street-urchin dance — all of it to erase the fabulous, dying-swan impression left by the act." And Cocteau, addressing himself to his fellow poets, sums it all up in two remarks. "Barbette's effect is instinctively calculated; we must transpose it into our own domain and use it deliberately." And, "The poet 'de-classes' everything and thus becomes a classic. Barbette mimics poetry itself, and this is his fascination. For his acrobatics are not really perilous. His affectations ought to be unbearable to us. The principle of his act embarrasses us. What is left, then? That thing he has created, going through its contortions under the spotlight."

The day after our talk in the coffee shop, I saw Barbette again, and this time his conversation consisted chiefly of anecdotes. Two of them turned on his favorite subject — refinement. His friend Princess Violette Murat, although ugly and obese, retained her "natural elegance," he said, even when being absurd — sniffing cocaine in her New York hotel room as she reproached her American sister-in-law, Princess Helena Murat, who had just returned from a Harlem nightclub, for leading an "unhealthy life." Whereas Mme. Aline, the severely black-clad manageress of a Marseilles brothel that Barbette, Cocteau, and Cocteau's friend Maurice Rostand (son of the dramatist, brother of the biologist) once visited in order to see its blue films, displayed her brand of refinement when replying to Cocteau's request for a homosexual film: "Ah, Monsieur, we do have a film of that kind, and everybody asks for it, but unfortunately it is being repaired. *Je suis désolée.*" Barbette's imitation of Mme. Aline's intonation, especially of the word *"dé-so-lée,"* and of her accompanying gesture of regret and apology — fingers of both hands joined under her chin — was a marvelous bit of mimicry; I could see what his "scabrous little scene" on the sofa might have been like. (During the showing of the only blue films available at Chez Aline, Barbette said, Maurice Rostand fell asleep and snored, and Cocteau kept up a commentary on the defects of the acting.)

It was with *The Blood of a Poet,* first publicly shown in 1932, that Cocteau, in many people's opinion, reached the highest point of his career — not that he declined steadily thereafter (he died in 1963), but even the most delightful of the later films, like *Orphée* and *La Belle et la Bête,* are not thought to rise, at least in poetic quality and imaginativeness, above the one in which Barbette substituted for the Vicomtesse de Noailles. Besides, in the thirties, between the Wall Street crash and the outbreak of war, great changes came over the artistic climate in which Cocteau — and Barbette, too — had been living. It was in the twenties and earliest thirties that both of them shone most brightly.

During the last hour I spent with Barbette, he spoke about the end of his performing career. The scar on his face, he told me, came from early falls and from an accident in Paris that was "not serious": one night at the Moulin Rouge, the backdrop curtain billowed out just as Barbette was about to plunge, the billow distracted him and he fell, and had to cancel the rest of the engagement. But later, in 1938, at Loew's State in New York, when he was sweating heavily after his act, he caught a chill in a backstage draft. When he awoke the next morning, he could hardly move, it was as though he had been "turned to stone" overnight in the position in which he had slept, and at Post-Graduate Hospital he was found to have pneumonia, along with a sudden crippling affliction of the bones and joints. The latter required surgery for rehabilitation; he spent eighteen months in the hospital and had to learn to walk again. Property he had bought in Texas had to be sold. Since then, he has been a trainer of performers — including performers in two acts of his own devising, which travel across the country — and he is serving as "aerial consultant" to a Disney spectacular called *Disney on Parade,* which will open in Chicago this Christmas.

Before we parted, Barbette gave me a list of people — most of them titled or otherwise elegant — whom I should see in Paris. I did see some of them later, and found that he was very well remembered indeed, in quite a variety of circles. In a Paris library I found a collection of reviews of his act by French magazine and newspaper critics. They all praised it for its beauty and delicacy, and their articles, marked by much discrimination, were of a higher level than one usually finds in reviews of popular entertainment. After seeing Barbette's act, the poet Paul Valéry, I discovered, wondered whether there wasn't a Greek myth called "Hercules Transformed into a Swallow." And the afternoon of December 19, 1930, at a "*Vendredi littéraire*" at the Lido on the Champs-Elysées — a party organized to promote a book by one of Barbette's admirers, the critic Gustave Fréjaville, about those Shakespearean boy actors of women's roles whose example had influenced Barbette in his original conception of his act — Barbette appeared "with the authorization of M. and Mme. Médrano" and recited, in English, the epilogue to *As You Like It*. Shakespeare wrote it to be spoken by the boy actor who played Rosalind, and it ends, "If I were a woman I would kiss as many of you as had beards that pleased me, complexions that liked me, and breaths that I defied not; and, I am sure, as many as have good beards, or good faces, or sweet breaths, will, for my kind offer, when I make curtsy, bid me farewell." Dressed demurely in white, Barbette "comported himself," one of the reviews said, "with an air of chaste simplicity that freed his performance of the slightest hint of bad taste. He was most enthusiastically applauded."

Barbette and I said good-bye on the sidewalk outside the Stephen F. Austin Hotel, and as Barbette moved away with his curious, careful, stiff walk, I felt that it was as though a part of the best years of Cocteau himself were vanishing. It is seldom, I suspect, that one can watch a poet's inspiration (for Cocteau, Barbette was a strange inspiration, perhaps, but an indubitable one) walking away in flesh and blood, bearing the wounds of his devotion to his art, along a Texas sidewalk.

(1966)

In Search
of True Cocteau

Francophilia, in America, is an unaccountable virus, striking even those who have no trace of France in their background. In my case the malady has taken a long course, determining several decades of work. The resulting biographies of French literary men have quite by chance, or so it seemed, occurred in chronological order: Gustave Flaubert and his *Madame Bovary;* Flaubert's "disciple" Guy de Maupassant and his stories (here an interruption for the seventeenth-century Grande Mademoiselle); the poet Guillaume Apollinaire (who died on the eve of the 1918 Armistice); and most lately Apollinaire's "lieutenant" in the arts, Jean Cocteau, who lived until 1963 and was poet, novelist, dramatist, cineast, portraitist, sculptor, and more besides. While Flaubert is the giant of those four, utterly absorbing in his art and in his incomparable letters, Cocteau has been the most pervasive.

Pervasive, I mean, of my own life while I wrote about him. That is not, I think, because Cocteau is the only one of the four whom I met in the flesh. (We encountered each other one single time, in the 1950's, at the dedication of the sculpture presented by Picasso in memory of Apollinaire, in the garden beside the church of Saint-Germain-des-Prés.) Partly it was because of the number of his surviving friends and enemies with whom I talked — their number, and their extreme variety, and the kaleidoscope of impressions Cocteau had made on them: everyone had a "conclusive," and different, opinion.

And always present was Cocteau's own style — his style of living, of writing, of inventing, that has given form to so many manifestations visible around one today. One is reminded at every turn of ways of dress prescribed by him for the casts of his plays and films, of the young people he invented in his books, especially in his novel *Les Enfants Terribles*, of his writing about his drug addiction, his cures, and the effects of both on his life and work.

The quest for Cocteau leads a biographer across continents, into contrasting quarters of capitals, into corners of widely separated provinces. Over the past five years he has come to seem to me rather like a diamond in the workshop, giving off ever greater brilliance as facet after facet is cut; or like a painting by a master that one thinks, after a time, one knows well, but that persists in surprising and fascinating with unsuspected, ever-renewed subtleties and effects.

To become sufficiently acquainted with his subject, a biographer must saturate himself in the man's work, his existence, and his times, becoming familiar — almost as in his own life — with the most trivial day-by-day details as well as with the great watersheds and dramas, acquiring amounts of information far exceeding those facts that will eventually be explicitly stated in his pages. Some of this will be discarded, but much will be invaluably present between the lines or in inflections, cadences, turns of phrase. Among the people interviewed there must be many whose association with the subject was only tangential: their evidence will frequently confirm or illuminate.

As it happened, my first biographical revelation of Cocteau came from one who was a major presence in his life. One spring afternoon in 1966, in Hollywood, in the home of Igor Stravinsky, with Picasso's famous pencil portrait of the composer looking down at us, Mr. Stravinsky handed me an orange folder, labeled: "Irritating and futile correspondence with J. Cocteau (and many others) on the subject of the first performance of *Oedipus*, in which many people wanted to have their say, and which considerably frayed my nerves. Igor Stravinsky."

Stravinsky had known Cocteau for over half a century, and his opinions about him ran the gamut: the very young Cocteau had annoyed him as a brash nuisance; in middle years he secured his collaboration as the librettist of *Oedipus Rex;* he greatly admired his drawings; and in 1963 his sarcasms about Cocteau's "publicity even in dying" were mingled with tears. (For Cocteau, Stravinsky was one of his "great encounters," the *Rite of Spring* one of his liberating artistic experiences.) The Stravinsky dossier was the first cluster of unpublished material to show that there was revelatory new light to be cast on Cocteau.

That my life of Cocteau needed to be written was the unequivocal opinion expressed a month or two later by André Maurois in his flat in Paris overlooking the Bois de Boulogne. There he and Madame Maurois — both of those kind and learned people have since died — gathered together for me several times at lunch friends and acquaintances of theirs and Cocteau's and let me discover for myself, in their conversation, in their respect for Cocteau's work, in their offers of letters and reminiscences, how much there was to be done.

"A big subject," André Maurois said. "There aren't many big literary biographical subjects left. And a controversial, paradoxical one. One must have the necessary detachment." Admirer that I am of Maurois's biographies, I wonder what he would think of the result of his encouragement.

The Mauroises' guests included people who had known

Cocteau well at all ages, in many guises. One day there were two ladies, elderly in years though not in spirit. The Rumanian-born Princess Marthe Bibesco, dressed on that occasion rather like an Amazon (when I saw her in her own home she was robed like a nun), had been Cocteau's friend from the time he flew with the aviator Garros in World War I; she had inherited from her friend the Abbé Mugnier all Cocteau's letters to that witty, worldly cleric.

The nonagenarian actress Simone, who had played on many stages in both French and English, I found to be a veritable Ninon de Lenclos of Parisian attractiveness and intelligence; she had known Cocteau even earlier, before she herself was engaged to Alain-Fournier, author of the celebrated novel *Le Grand Meaulnes*, killed in action in 1914. She told me about the actor De Max, of the Comédie Française, who had organized Cocteau's literary debut at a poetry-reading in 1908.

Another day there were two young men. Edouard Dermit, in his adolescence a coal miner in the Ardennes, had come to Paris when barely twenty and been engaged by Cocteau as a gardener; then he acted in several of his films and had become his inseparable companion. Cocteau made him his principal heir, and today he is the arbiter of who may, and who may not, use the Cocteau archives. Very different was Pierre Georgel, a serious, attractive young scholar who was what might be called Cocteau's literary aide-de-camp in his last years; it was Georgel who assembled the excellent posthumous Cocteau exhibition at the Jacquemart-André Museum in 1965, and he is probably the living person most familiar with every page of Cocteau's many works.

To the Maurois' came what the French call "*le Tout-Paris.*" One day the poet and novelist Louise de Vilmorin began abruptly at table to execrate "that woman who took Cocteau away from me"; out from her lovely eyes rushed amazing quantities of real tears; she cried "*O Jean! Mon Jean!*" and sobbed aloud. Everyone present knew that in a recent interview Mlle. de Vilmorin had said that she and Cocteau had contemplated marriage; everyone knew who the "other woman" was; everyone knew how chimerical the unmarriageable Cocteau's "proposals of marriage" could only be.

As abruptly as they had begun, Mlle. de Vilmorin's tears stopped; in a moment she was calmly eating her ice cream. (It was Louise de Vilmorin who shortly before her death last winter is said to have retorted to a reporter who asked whether she was going to marry her great friend André Malraux: "How out of date you are! Don't you know nowadays it's only priests who get married?") At another Maurois lunch a French Academician claimed to have seen or been told of Cocteau's secret police dossier, and it bore the official tag: "*Cocteau, Jean.* Opium addict. Pederast. (Says he is a poet.)"

Out from the Maurois' elegant rooms, the Cocteau trail led in many directions. To a shabby shop behind the Gare Montparnasse, where the good-natured proprietor let a constant stream of neighborhood boys walk in and out borrowing and returning items from his vast archive of comic books that is a well-known mecca for collectors. He showed me a bit of his tattooing, which he said was *très spécial,* extending from wrist to ankle, back and front," and which Cocteau used to invite him to show off to friends. He spoke of Cocteau's love of novelty, and hazarded the guess that had he lived a few years longer, he would have begun to write and draw some form of comic books of his own. Perhaps so, perhaps not: but the tattooed bookseller, dealer in what the French call *bandes dessinées,* was not the only acquaintance of Cocteau's I met who found it natural to associate him with something he hadn't tried *yet;* his love of experiment was well recognized.

In her hotel, which was also mine, Mlle. Gabrielle Chanel, who paid for a number of Cocteau's drug cures over a span of many years, gave me her mercurial opinions of him, some of them excoriating, others affectionate; the conversations — monologues, rather, in her rough, husky voice — were conducted by telephone between our nearly adjacent rooms. Mlle. Chanel claimed to dislike speaking of the past; but her monologues were not, luckily for me, particularly brief. In another hotel, in a narrow Left Bank street, an elegantly mannered, threadbare, ashen-faced man who didn't hide his hypodermic, recounted some of Cocteau's early meetings with the convict-poet Jean Genet, who had been his, my informant's, friend as well.

In his flat off the Etoile, Maurice Goudeket, Cocteau's schoolmate, Colette's widower, in his seventies newly re-married and the father of a small son whose godfather was Cocteau, told me, among much else testifying to the fun of Cocteau's company, about boasting to Cocteau of the boy's precocity: "He's been walking since he was six months old." Cocteau's retort: "Where is he now?"

It is a biographer's good fortune when those connected with his subject want their friend to be properly known. Comte Henri de Beaumont had typed out for me copies of Cocteau's side of a forty-year correspondence with his uncle, Etienne de Beaumont, the original of Raymond Radiguet's character the Comte d'Orgel, famous for his costume balls, Maecenas of the arts — with whose Red Cross ambulances Cocteau had served in 1916; beside the copies, on the writing table in the Beaumont chateau in Normandy, lay the letters themselves.

At the other end of France, in his Mas de Fourques, between Nîmes and Montpellier, where dozens of peacocks stroll the garden paths and nest in the cedars in the evenings, the artist Jean Hugo (great-grandson of the poet) had copied for me, in beautiful handwriting, extracts from his diary kept during the 1920's when he and his first wife Valentine designed sets and costumes for Cocteau's plays and saw him almost daily. Valen-tine Hugo herself, friend of the Surrealists and in old age still a great beauty — Cocteau called her his "swan" — in her plant-filled flat on the Place Victor-Hugo in Paris, gave me bundles of photocopies of Cocteau's early letters with her own pungent glosses in the margins.

To Cocteau the expression "generation gap" would have been meaningless; he valued high spirits in all the ages of man; the span of years among his friends was always immense. In Fiesole the long-expatriate American painter Romaine Brooks, almost one hundred, told me that half a century ago she found the youthful Cocteau a cooperative poser for his portrait against an Eiffel Tower background (now hanging in the Musée National d'Art Moderne in Paris) as long as she fed him slices of chocolate cake; and one afternoon in New York there came to call two of Cocteau's youngest friends, Emilienne Dermit (Edouard's sister) and her schoolmate Carole Weisweiller. (It was with Carole's mother, Mme. Francine Weisweiller, that Cocteau and Edouard Dermit had lived for ten years in her Villa Santo Sospir at Cap Ferrat, and who appears, wearing a Victorian gown by Balenciaga, in Cocteau's last film *Le Testament d'Orphée*.)

Three dancers from Cocteau's ballets with whom I spoke — Serge Lifar in Cannes, Léonide Massine on his island off Positano, and Maria Chabelska on Claremont Avenue (she created the role of the American girl in *Parade* in 1917) — are all of them still at work; and so is Barbette, the Texan female-impersonator who dazzled Cocteau with his performance on the tightrope in the 1920's and inspired some of his best writings on the nature of art. Acting in films in Rome I found Leo Coleman, the original boy Toby in Gian Carlo Menotti's *The Medium*, who posed with Cocteau for fantastic photos made by Philippe Halsman for *Life* magazine in 1949. And so it went.

But Cocteau was pervasive in ways other than through his own works and their present-day manifestations and through the variety, articulateness and generosity of his friends of many nationalities, including a number of Americans. The radioactive qualities that made his life so *mouvementée* spilled over into posthumous drama.

None of my other biographies had brought me anonymous telephone calls or threatening letters. There are always those who consider an artist their exclusive property — that is, to be limited, in treatment, to the only terms in which they themselves were acquainted with him or can comprehend him. (A certain type of academic, on the other hand — a type I am assured is rare — seems hardly able to tolerate the idea that an artist is made of flesh and blood.) In Cocteau's case there was a degree of homosexual alarm — warnings to keep off the reservation, threats to an "outsider," charges of ignorance and hostility, rigid distinctions between gay and square. (Not in France, I should add, where a wide range of human feelings is taken for granted.)

Several New York literati, surprisingly unacquainted with Cocteau's works, nevertheless favored me with monologues on his "unsatisfactory" nature. There is, I found, a certain dismay set up by almost any mention of Cocteau — a dismay caused by his candid admissions (not *all* of them exhibitionistic) that he was not altogether virtuous. We in Anglo-Saxon countries tend perhaps to be unnerved less by a show of bad character than by the absence of any claim to goodness. It is somewhat our style to condone misconduct as long as it is accompanied by protestations of lofty motives. Cocteau knew his flaws. He seldom denied them, seldom justified them. Nor did he usually expect them to add to his appeal. On occasion he would flaunt them to shock or to amuse, and at such times he could be either silly or dazzling.

Cocteau disliked consistency, ideologies. He would have agreed with Saul Bellow's recent comment that "Ideology is a drag." He once said: "To give yourself wholly to each particular case, even if this involves you in a series of seeming contradictions, puts you on a straighter course and gives you deeper insights than abstract principles, which so often force you to be untrue to what is best in yourself."

Cocteau in his teens running away from his bourgeois family to live in the underworld of Marseilles; Cocteau playing the drums in a jazz band; Cocteau writing noble versions of *Antigone*, of *Oedipus*; Cocteau at Midnight Mass between opium pipes; Cocteau, tormented by Radiguet's death, staring for weeks at his own face in a mirror; the Cocteau of the films *The Blood of a Poet*, *Orpheus*, *Beauty and the Beast*, and of his last long poem *Le Requiem* — there is nothing consistent there, and it is not the task of a biographer to compress it all into a neat pattern. It is only by giving full scope to all his subject's qualities that he can hope to extend his own view and most eloquently communicate it.

I never began a book more hesitantly than this one about the marvelous Cocteau; and never ended one more fascinated by the artist who was my subject.

(1970)

A Burial in Venice

Venice, April 17, 1971

A number of those who saw the procession of gondolas, each rowed by two gondoliers and each bearing five passengers, crossing the Venetian lagoon early in the afternoon of April 15 behind the funeral barge carrying the body of Igor Stravinsky to the island cemetery of San Michele remarked that it must have resembled that other procession of gondolas, chronicled in biographies of Stravinsky's friend and patron Sergei Diaghilev, impresario of the Ballets Russes, which on an August day in 1929 followed Diaghilev's body to the same resting place. Physically, no doubt, the two corteges were similar — the black file of gondolas silhouetted against a background of total blue (for even in these days of pollution the blue of the Venetian sky can be so intense as to dye the water that reflects it), the casket on the barge flower-covered — and probably as the first of the Diaghilev gondolas approached the San Michele landing stage there stood in it, as

269

there did in the leading gondola this time, a figure in vestments and tall black headdress with an acolyte holding up a cross: a priest of the Greek Orthodox Church. The bodies of both men were destined for a remote corner of the cemetery separated from the rest by a gate, usually locked, marked "Rito Greco," and for the rare burials there an Orthodox priest must cross the lagoon, all the clergy attached to the funeral church on San Michele itself being Roman Catholics. The Greek enclosure is far less formal in appearance than the rest of the cemetery — in fact, something of a tangle. An overgrown garden shaded with cypresses and laurels, it is at the outer edge of the island; and the lagoon, lapping its wall, is visible through arched grilles. Here one may wander among stones that bear the names Troubetzkoy, Potëmkin, Bagration. Both Diaghilev and Stravinsky had long been self-exiled from their native Russia, and both had drawn inspiration from Venice. Although the Ballets Russes never performed here, Diaghilev spent many of his summers on the Lido, usually with Nijinsky or Lifar or some of his other favorites and principal dancers, planning future ballets. Stravinsky dedicated one of his works, the *Canticum Sacrum*, to Venice and St. Mark; he chose the Venetian summer music festivals for its premiere and that of several other works, including *The Rake's Progress;* and he conducted many concerts here and often spoke of the city with love.

And yet the contrasting circumstances of the Venetian burials of those two Russian friends are at least as striking as the obvious similarities. Diaghilev was devoted to the art of the dance, and his genius as impresario lay in his inspired exploitation of artists (he was quick to appreciate the early Stravinsky — the Stravinsky of *The Firebird, Petrouchka*, and *The Rite of Spring*); he was not an artist himself. Nor was he deeply religious — rather, superstitious. Warned by a fortune-teller that he would die on the water, he dreaded even taking his dancers from France across the English Channel, and he did die "on" the water — died while vacationing at the Lido-Bains Hotel, and his burial in Venice was somewhat fortuitous.

Stravinsky, who was a profoundly religious man, died in New York, early on the morning of April 6, after several years of bad health. And here in Venice the large posters that very soon thereafter appeared in profusion on walls and in other public places throughout the city told the story, in an Italianate proclamation printed in black and purple on a white ground, of his carefully considered wish:

> THE CITY OF VENICE DOES HOMAGE TO THE REMAINS OF THE GREAT MUSICIAN IGOR STRAVINSKY, WHO IN A GESTURE OF EXQUISITE FRIENDSHIP ASKED TO BE BURIED IN THE CITY WHICH HE LOVED ABOVE ALL OTHERS.

What the Venetian municipal authorities had done on learning of Stravinsky's wish was to offer for his funeral service the immense Church of Santi Giovanni e Paolo (known locally by the contraction "San Zanipolo"), which is even larger than St. Mark's, and is perhaps more suitable than St. Mark's for such a rite, because of its historic role as a burying place of the doges (also, of the largest Venetian churches it is the closest to the cemetery), and they offered as well, for the performance of whatever music might be chosen, the orchestra of the city's beautiful Fenice Theatre and the Polyphonic Choir of Radiodiffusione Italiana. Such elements, combined and elaborated with the Italian gift for splendor and drama, could scarcely fail to result in something impressive, and it was, in fact, after a religious ceremony of great magnificence and singularity that that file of gondolas crossed the lagoon to San Michele.

Santi Giovanni e Paolo, beside a canal, is a towering Gothic church, best known to tourists for the commanding fifteenth-century equestrian statue of the *condottiere* Bartolomeo Colleoni by the sculptors Verrocchio and Leopardi that stands in the square just outside; within, along with its stained glass and countless monuments to the doges, it is scarcely less than a museum of paintings, by Giovanni Bellini, Lorenzo Lotto, and Paolo Veronese. The several Veroneses are on the ceiling of a large chapel off the main body of the church, and it was here that Stravinsky's coffin was brought on the fourteenth, after being transported from New York to Fiumicino Airport in Rome and thence by hearse and ferry to Venice. The black-and-purple posters spelled out for the citizenry the exact time of its arrival; as a result, all afternoon and evening lines of Venetians of all ages — there were many children, perhaps brought in order to be told later what they had seen — filed through the chapel, where four tall tapers flickered at the corners of the bier. Before the principal ceremony, at noon the next day, there was brief early-morning prayer while the bier was brought before the main altar of the church; this was attended by family, friends, and a few others. Among the mourners was a gray-haired ancient who, sitting with a woman companion, did not leave at the end but remained, almost motionless, in his seat throughout the morning as the church gradually filled to overflowing. Not everyone recognized him as Ezra Pound.

The piece of Stravinsky's religious music chosen for the occasion by the conductor Robert Craft, the composer's much younger American friend and associate, and co-author with him of a series of pungent volumes of reflection and conversation, was (after a brief choral requiem by Alessandro Scarlatti) the *Requiem Canticles*, Stravinsky's last considerable work, completed in 1966, when he was eighty-four. It was shortly after the premiere of the *Requiem Canticles* that what proved to be Stravinsky's long final illness began, and it has often been suggested that in writing the *Canticles* he was more or less consciously composing his own requiem. (In conversation, however, Stravinsky's friends recall, he always tended to speak more of life than of death. A few years ago, when a young interviewer asked him if he found inspiration "less fluent in old age," his genial reply was "I suppose for you I am in old age. For me, I just happen to be in my eighties." And at bad moments during the past year or two when he sometimes called for his wife or another member of his household and was asked, "What is it you need?" he would reply, "To be assured of my own existence." The assurance might take the form of a kiss, a handclasp, or merely the playing of a favorite record.)

The *Requiem Canticles* is a moving but difficult work, with much soft playing by strings, whose sounds emerged thinly from the deep apse of Santi Giovanni e Paolo, where orchestra and choir were placed, and the spoken portions came forth less resonantly than those parts scored for singing. One suspects that even Craft himself, who conducted the *Requiem Canticles* out of admiration and piety, discovered the day's greatest musical effectiveness — owing in large part to the church's architecture, and as contrasted with intrinsic musical greatness — in what came after the *Requiem Canticles* ended: the Orthodox Requiem.

Down the center aisle from the basilica's great front door, which was left open to the sunny day, there appeared, flanked by acolytes, a theatrically handsome ecclesiastic: young, olive-skinned, black-bearded, with finely cut features, almond eyes, and an expression of scarcely credible serenity, wearing a tall black headdress and brilliant gold vestments — the Archimandrite of Venice, leader of the city's Greek Orthodox congregation. Everyone recognized his presence as officiating priest in this church, which was founded by Dominicans and is still in their charge, as an ecumenical event: he had been invited by the Cardinal Patriarch of St. Mark's, one of whose auxiliaries, a Roman Catholic bishop, with a violet zucchetto on his head, sat near the altar as host.

The golden Archimandrite blessed the congregation from the steps of the high Gothic presbytery; standing there against the background of the massed, now silent musicians ranged in tiers before the altar, the altar rail itself guarded by a pair of bicorned, red-pomponed carabinieri, each with hand on sword, he began to chant in Greek. For half an hour, he chanted almost uninterruptedly to the three thousand in the church and those standing outside the doors; those in the church stood, too, as is the Orthodox way. The many musicians present were unanimous in finding the Archimandrite an astonishing virtuoso in the art of sacred chant, extraordinary in his refinement of modulation and phrasing; there was unchanging, ineffable calm in the arresting face as he chanted the service, which contained, we were told, psalms and beatitudes as well as Epistle and Gospel, moving without apparent effort from deep tones to falsetto, from pianissimo to forte, occasionally signaling by a glance to the organist above. He chanted still as he descended the steps, walked entirely around the bier, swinging his smoking censer, blessing Stravinsky, the Stravinsky family, and all the congregation, and finally beckoned the members of the family to come from their seats to kiss the coffin.

Preceded by the Archimandrite, the bishop, the coffin, and the inevitable outsize floral pieces, family and friends walked up the center aisle and out to the waiting gondolas. The scene without was like one of Carpaccio's pageants, with accents of today. Every window in the old houses lining the square and the canal and every bridge was filled with watching Venetians, and the floral pieces standing in the sun against the base of the statue of the haughty Renaissance warrior bore inscriptions ranging from a red-ribboned salute from the artists of the Soviet Union to the Stravinsky grandchildren's "*A Grandpère bien aimé.*"

One of the floral pieces had been contributed by the Municipality of Venice, and during the preparation and execution of the ceremonies there were a few moments when one was aware of the bureaucratic hand. Venice, which, as everyone knows, is at present existing precariously, threatened with destruction by pollution and tides, owes much of what prosperity it has to tourism; and although it may sound ungracious to say so, the municipality was scarcely unaware that a last great tribute to the world-famous composer could not fail to bring to Venice, if only for a day or two, a large number of visitors from abroad — journalists, musicians, and others — during the slack season following Easter.

The city-sponsored concert and Requiem in Santi Giovanni e Paolo were open to the public, and for a few moments between the Scarlatti and the *Requiem Canticles* the mayor of Venice read a brief official tribute. But the invitations to that event, mailed to a certain number of Italians and foreigners, contained a few words that the municipality omitted from its widely distributed posters: the final events — the ceremony of absolution that was to take place in the Orthodox chapel in a remote corner of the cemetery and the burial itself — were to be performed only "in the presence of members of the family and intimate friends." As a result, Venetians and tourists who had seen the posters but not the invitations and had come to the cemetery had to be turned away. In the tiny Orthodox chapel, the marvelous calm Archimandrite himself assumed bureaucratic guise for a few moments, when the waiting and tired family found him, in his black cassock, combing his hair and beard behind a curtain instead of proceeding with the absolution; supported by a municipal official who had accompanied him, he protested, with flashing eyes and in voluble Italian (his name is Cherubino Malissianos), that it would be unthinkable to absolve Igor Stravinsky of his sins without the presence of the mayor (whom the family had not invited to this private ceremony, but who, it seems, had announced his intention of coming anyway, somewhat later). The family prevailed, however, and the prelate resumed his golden vestments and, with marvelous simultaneity, his full archimandrital personality. Absolution was exquisitely intoned. And at the grave among the trees members of the family sprinkled earth on the coffin to the accompaniment of final chanting.

Before returning to the landing stage, some paid a visit to the grave of Diaghilev, a few yards from Stravinsky's. That morning, the Venetian newspaper *Il Gazzettino* had contained an article by the Italian composer Gian Francesco Malipiero, a man not noted for subtlety, who wondered in print why Stravinsky had chosen to be buried in Venice: "Was it perhaps to forget Hollywood? Or to be reconciled with Diaghilev?" (Collaboration between composer and impresario had not always been smooth.) On Diaghilev's gravestone there

275

are incised a few words in Russian that seemed to provide a sufficient retort to Malipiero's foolishness. They are Diaghilev's own words, quite simple, and might apply equally to the two famous men: "Venice, our eternal inspiration and bringer of peace."